D1576770

# Elliptic Integrals

## *by Harris Hancock*

**DOVER PUBLICATIONS, INC., NEW YORK,**

Manufactuerd in United States of America

Dover Publications, Inc.
920 Broadway
New York 10, N. Y.

# CONTENTS

# INTRODUCTION

THE editors of the present series of mathematical monographs have requested me to write a work on elliptic integrals which "shall relate almost entirely to the three well-known elliptic integrals, with tables and examples showing practical applications, and which shall fill about one hundred octavo pages." In complying with their request, I shall limit the monograph to what is known as the Legendre-Jacobi theory; and to keep the work within the desired number of pages I must confine the discussion almost entirely to what is known as the elliptic integrals of the first and second kinds.

In the elementary calculus are found methods of integrating any rational expression involving under a square root sign a quadratic in one variable; in the present work, which may be regarded as a somewhat more advanced calculus, we have to integrate similar expressions where cubics and quartics in one variable occur under the root sign. Whatever be the nature of these cubics and quartics, it will be seen that the integrals may be transformed into standard normal forms. Tables are given of these normal forms, so that the integral in question may be calculated to any degree of exactness required.

With the trigonometric sine function is associated its inverse function, an integral; and similarly with the normal forms of elliptic integrals there are associated elliptic functions. A short account is given of these functions which emphasizes their doubly periodic properties. By making suitable transformations and using the inverse of these functions, it is found that the integrals in question may be expressed more concisely through the normal forms and in a manner that indicates the transformation employed.

5

The underlying theory, the philosophy of the subject, I have attempted to give in my larger work on elliptic functions, Vol. I. In the preparation of the present monograph much use has been made of Greenhill's *Application of Elliptic Functions*, a work which cannot be commended too highly; one may also read with great advantage Cayley's *Elliptic Functions*. The standard works of Legendre, Abel and Jacobi are briefly considered in the text. It may also be of interest to note briefly the earlier mathematicians who made possible the writings just mentioned.

The difference of two arcs of an ellipse that do not overlap may be expressed through the difference of two lengths on a straight line; in other words, this difference may be expressed in an *algebraic* manner. This is the geometrical signification of a theorem due to an Italian mathematician, Fagnano, which theorem is published in the twenty-sixth volume of the *Giornale de' letterari d'Italia*, 1716, and later with numerous other mathematical papers in two volumes under the title *Produzioni mathematiche del Marchese Giulio Carlo de' Toschi di Fagnano*, 1750.

The great French mathematician Hermite (*Cours*, rédigé par Andoyer, Paris, 1882) writes "*Ce résultat doit être cité avec admiration comme ayant ouvert le premier la voie à la théorie des fonctions elliptiques.*"

Maclaurin in his celebrated work *A Treatise on Fluxions*, Edinburgh, 1742, Vol. II, p. 745, shows " how the *elastic curve* may be constructed in all cases by the rectification of the conic sections." On p. 744 he gives Jacob Bernoulli " as the celebrated author who first resolved this as well as several other curious problems " (see *Acta Eruditorium*, 1694, p. 274). It is thus seen that the elliptic integrals made their appearance in the formative period of the integral calculus.

The results that are given in Maclaurin's work were simplified and extended by d'Alembert in his treatise *Recherches sur le calcul intégral. Histoire de l'Ac. de Berlin, Année* 1746, pp. 182–224. The second part of this work, *Des différentielles qui se rapportent à la rectification de l'ellipse ou de l'hyperbole*, treats of a number of differentials whose integrals through simple substitutions reduce to the integrals through which the arc of an ellipse or hyperbola may be expressed.

It was also known through the works of Fagnano, Jacob Bernoulli and others that the expressions for $\sin(\alpha+\beta)$, $\sin(\alpha-\beta)$ etc., gave a means of adding or subtracting the arcs of circles, and that between the limits of two integrals that express lengths of arc of a lemniscate an algebraic relation exists, such that the arc of a lemniscate, although a transcendent of higher order, may be doubled or halved just as the arc of a circle by means of geometric construction.

It was natural to inquire if the ellipse, hyperbola, etc., did not have similar properties. Investigating such properties, Euler made the remarkable discovery of the addition-theorem of elliptic integrals (see *Nov. Comm. Petrop.*, VI, pp. 58–84, 1761; and VII, p. 3; VIII, p. 83). A direct proof of this theorem was later given by Lagrange and in a manner which elicited the great admiration of Euler (see Serret's *Œuvres de Lagrange*, *T*. II, p. 533).

The addition-theorem for elliptic integrals gave to the elliptic functions a meaning in higher analysis similar to that which the cyclometric and logarithmic functions had enjoyed for a long time.

I regret that space does not permit the derivation of these addition-theorems and that the reader must be referred to a larger work.

The above mathematicians are the ones to whom Legendre refers in the introduction of his *Traité des fonctions elliptiques*, published in three quarto volumes, Paris, 1825. This work must always be regarded as the foundation of the theory of elliptic integrals and their associated functions; and Legendre must be regarded as the founder of this theory, for upon his investigations were established the doubly periodic properties of these functions by Abel and Jacobi and indeed in the very form given by Legendre. Short accounts of these theories are found in the sequel.

For more extended works the reader is referred to Appell

et Lacour, *Fonctions elliptiques*, and to Enneper, *Elliptische Funktionen*, where in particular the historical notes and list of authors cited on pp. 500–598 are valuable. Fricke in the article " *Elliptische Funktionen*," *Encylcopädie der mathematischen Wissenschaften*, Vol. II, gives a fairly complete list of books and monographs that have been written on this subject.

To Dr. Mansfield Merriman I am indebted for suggesting many of the problems of Chapter V and also for valuable assistance in editing this work. I have pleasure also in thanking my colleague, Dr. Edward S. Smith, for drawing the figures carefully to scale.

HARRIS HANCOCK.

2365 Auburn Ave.,
CINCINNATI, OHIO,
October 3, 1916.

# ELLIPTIC INTEGRALS

## CHAPTER I

### ELLIPTIC INTEGRALS OF THE FIRST, SECOND AND THIRD KINDS. THE LEGENDRE TRANSFORMATION

**Art. 1.** In the elementary calculus are studied such integrals as $\int \dfrac{dx}{s}$, $\int \dfrac{x\,dx}{(ax+b)s}$, etc., where $s^2 = ax^2 + 2bx + c$. In general the integral of any rational function of $x$ and $s$ can be transformed into other typical integrals, which are readily integrable. Such types of integrals are

$$\int^x \frac{dx}{\sqrt{1-x^2}}, \quad \int_0^1 \frac{dx}{\sqrt{1-x^2}}, \quad \int_0^x \frac{dx}{\sqrt{x^2+1}}, \quad \text{etc.}$$

In the present theory instead of, as above, writing $s^2$ equal to a quadratic in $x$, we shall put $s^2$ equal to a cubic or quartic in $x$. Suppose further that $F(x, s)$ is any rational function of $x$ and $s$ and consider the integral $\int F(x, s)dx$. Such an integral may be made to depend upon three types of integral of the form

$$\int \frac{dx}{s}, \quad \int \frac{x^2 dx}{s} \quad \text{and} \quad \int \frac{dx}{(x-b)s}.$$

These three types of integral, in somewhat different notation, were designated by Legendre, the founder of this theory, as elliptic integrals of the *first*, *second*, and *third kinds* respectively, while the general term "elliptic integral" was given by him to any integral of the form $\int F(x, s)dx$  The method of expressing the general integral through the three types of integral as first indicated by Legendre, may be found in my *Elliptic Functions*, Vol. I, p. 180.

**Art. 2.** First consider integrals of the form

$$\int \frac{dx}{\sqrt{R(x)}}, \qquad \ldots \qquad (1)$$

which, as will be shown, reduce to a definite typical normal form,* when $R(x)$ is either of the third or fourth degree in $x$.

Suppose that $R(x)$ is of the fourth degree, and write

$$R(x) = a_0 x^4 + a_1 x^3 + a_2 x^2 + a_3 x + a_4,$$

where $a_0, a_1, \ldots,$ are real constants. It is seen that (1) may be written

$$\frac{1}{\sqrt{a_0}} \int \frac{dx}{\sqrt{X}}, \qquad \ldots \qquad (2)$$

where $X$, when decomposed into its factors, is

$$X = \pm (x - \alpha)(x - \beta)(x - \gamma)(x - \delta),$$

and $\sqrt{a_0}$ is a real quantity. If the roots are all real, suppose that $\alpha > \beta > \gamma > \delta$; if two are complex, take $\alpha$ and $\beta$ real and write $\gamma = \rho + i\sigma$, $\delta = \rho - i\sigma$, where $i = \sqrt{-1}$; and if all four of the roots are complex, denote them by $\alpha = \mu + i\nu$, $\beta = \mu - i\nu$, $\gamma = \rho + i\sigma$, $\delta = \rho - i\sigma$.

In the present work the variable is taken real unless it is stated to the contrary or is otherwise evident.

We shall first so transform the expression $X$ that only *even* powers of the variable appear. With Legendre (loc. cit., p. 7), write

$$x = \frac{p + qy}{1 + y}. \qquad \ldots \qquad (3)$$

It follows at once that

$$\frac{dx}{\sqrt{X}} = \frac{(q - p)dy}{\sqrt{\pm Y}}, \qquad \ldots \qquad (4)$$

---

* See Legendre, *Traité des fonctions elliptiques*, T. I., p. 11, et seq.; Richelot, *Crelle*, Bd. 34, p. 1; Enneper, *Elliptische Functionen*, p. 14.

where

$$Y=[p-\alpha+(q-\alpha)y][p-\beta+(q-\beta)y][p-\gamma+(q-\gamma)y][p-\delta+(q-\delta)y].$$
$$(5)$$

As all the results must be real, it will be seen that real values may be given to $p$ and $q$ in such a way that only even powers of $y$ appear on the right-hand side of (5). If in this expression we multiply the first and second factors together, we have

$$(p-\alpha)(p-\beta)+(q-\alpha)(q-\beta)y^2$$

provided

$$(p-\alpha)(q-\beta)+(p-\beta)(q-\alpha)=0; \quad \ldots \quad (6)$$

and similarly if

$$(p-\gamma)(q-\delta)+(p-\delta)(q-\gamma)=0, \quad \ldots \quad (7)$$

the product of the third and fourth factors of (5) is

$$(p-\gamma)(p-\delta)+(q-\gamma)(q-\delta)y^2.$$

From (6) and (7) it follows that

$$pq+\alpha\beta=\frac{p+q}{2}(\alpha+\beta),$$

and

$$pq+\gamma\delta=\frac{p+q}{2}(\gamma+\delta).$$

From the last two equations, it also follows that

$$\frac{p+q}{2}=\frac{\alpha\beta-\gamma\delta}{\alpha+\beta-\gamma-\delta}, \quad pq=\frac{\alpha\beta(\gamma+\delta)-\gamma\delta(\alpha+\beta)}{\alpha+\beta-\gamma-\delta}. \quad . \quad (8)$$

From (8) it is seen that the sum and quotient of $p$ and $q$ are real quantities whatever the nature of the four roots $\alpha$, $\beta$, $\gamma$, and $\delta$ may be; and further from (8) it is seen that

$$\left(\frac{q-p}{2}\right)^2=\frac{(\alpha-\gamma)(\alpha-\delta)(\beta-\gamma)(\beta-\delta)}{(\alpha+\beta-\gamma-\delta)^2}, \quad . \quad . \quad (9)$$

which is always a positive quantity. It follows that $q-p$ is a real quantity, and that $p$ and $q$ are real.

The equations (8) and (9) cannot be used if $\alpha+\beta=\gamma+\delta$.

In this case, as is readily shown, instead of the substitution (3), we may write

$$x = y + \frac{\alpha + \beta}{2} = y + \frac{\gamma + \delta}{2}.$$

It follows that (5) takes the form

$$Y = (\pm m^2 \pm n^2 y^2)(\pm r^2 \pm l^2 y^2),$$

where $m$, $n$, $r$, and $l$ are real quantities.

The expression (4) then becomes

$$\frac{dx}{\sqrt{X}} = \frac{(q-p)dy}{\sqrt{\pm Y}} = \frac{dy}{f\sqrt{\pm(1 \pm g^2 y^2)(1 \pm h^2 y^2)}}, \quad . \quad . \quad (10)$$

where $f$, $g$, and $h$ are essentially real quantities.

In the expression on the right-hand side, suppose that $h > g$ and put $hy = t$, and $\frac{g}{h} = c$, where $c < 1$.

It follows that

$$\frac{dx}{\sqrt{X}} = \frac{dt}{fh\sqrt{\pm(1 \pm t^2)(1 \pm c^2 t^2)}}. \quad . \quad . \quad . \quad (11)$$

It is seen that under the radical there are eight combinations of sign. With Legendre, loc. cit., Chap. II, and *Enneper*, p. 17, a table will be given below from which it is seen that the corresponding functions may be expressed by means of trigonometric substitutions in the one normal form

$$\frac{dx}{\sqrt{X}} = \pm \frac{1}{M} \frac{d\phi}{\sqrt{1 - k^2 \sin^2 \phi}} = \pm \frac{1}{M} \frac{dv}{\sqrt{(1-v^2)(1-k^2v^2)}}, \quad . \quad (12)$$

where $M$ is a *real* quantity and $v = \sin \phi$.

The quantity $k$, called the *modulus*, is also real, and situated within the interval $o \leq k \leq 1$.

Of the expressions under the root sign $\sqrt{-(1+t^2)(1+c^2t^2)}$ may be neglected, since $R(x)$, assumed to be positive for at least some real value of the original $x$, cannot be transformed into a function that is always negative by a real substitution.

**Art. 3.** Writing $\Delta\phi = \sqrt{1 - k^2 \sin^2 \phi}$ and defining the *com-*

*plementary modulus* $k'$ by the relation $k^2+k'^2=1$, the following table results:

I. $\dfrac{dt}{\sqrt{(1+t^2)(1+c^2t^2)}}=\dfrac{d\phi}{\Delta\phi}$, $\qquad t=\tan\phi$, $\qquad k^2=1-c^2$

II. $\dfrac{dt}{\sqrt{(1-t^2)(1+c^2t^2)}}=\dfrac{-k'd\phi}{\Delta\phi}$, $\quad t=\cos\phi$, $\qquad k^2=\dfrac{c^2}{1+c^2}$

III. $\dfrac{dt}{\sqrt{(t^2-1)(1+c^2t^2)}}=\dfrac{k\,d\phi}{\Delta\phi}$, $\qquad t=\sec\phi$, $\qquad k^2=\dfrac{1}{1+c^2}$

IV. $\dfrac{dt}{\sqrt{(1+t^2)(1-c^2t^2)}}=\dfrac{-k\,d\phi}{\Delta\phi}$, $\quad t=\dfrac{\cos\phi}{c}$, $\qquad k^2=\dfrac{1}{1+c^2}$

V. $\dfrac{dt}{\sqrt{(1+t^2)(c^2t^2-1)}}=\dfrac{k'd\phi}{\Delta\phi}$, $\qquad t=\dfrac{\sec\phi}{c}$, $\qquad k^2=\dfrac{c^2}{1+c^2}$

VI. $\dfrac{dt}{\sqrt{(1-t^2)(1-c^2t^2)}}=\dfrac{d\phi}{\Delta\phi}$, $\qquad t=\sin\phi$, $\qquad k^2=c^2$

VIa. $\dfrac{dt}{\sqrt{(t^2-1)(c^2t^2-1)}}=-\dfrac{d\phi}{\Delta\phi}$, $\quad t=\dfrac{1}{c\sin\phi}$, $\qquad k^2=c^2$

VII. $\dfrac{dt}{\sqrt{(t^2-1)(1-c^2t^2)}}=-\dfrac{d\phi}{\Delta\phi}$, $\quad t^2=\sin^2\phi+\dfrac{\cos^2\phi}{c^2}$, $\ k^2=1-c^2$

The formulas VI and VIa have the same form; in VI it is necessary that $t\leqq 1$, while in VIa it is required that $t\geqq\dfrac{1}{c}$.

**Art. 4.** It is seen that the eight transformations in the table are all of the form

$$t^2=\frac{A+B\sin^2\phi}{C+D\sin^2\phi}, \quad\cdots\cdots\quad (i)$$

where $A$, $B$, $C$, and $D$ are real constants; at the same time it is seen that by means of real substitutions the following reduction can always be made:

$$\frac{dx}{\sqrt{R(x)}}=\pm\frac{1}{M}\frac{d\phi}{\Delta\phi}=\pm\frac{1}{M}\frac{dv}{\sqrt{(1-v^2)(1-k^2v^2)}},$$

where $v = \sin \phi$.

These substitutions and reductions are given in full in Chap. III.

The radical in $\dfrac{dv}{\sqrt{(1-v^2)(1-k^2v^2)}}$ is *real* for real values of $v$ that are $1°$ less than unity and $2°$ greater than $\dfrac{1}{k}$. In the latter case, write $v = \dfrac{1}{ks}$, and then

$$\frac{dv}{\sqrt{(1-v^2)(1-k^2v^2)}} = - \frac{ds}{\sqrt{(1-s^2)(1-k^2s^2)}}.$$

In this substitution as $v$ passes from $\dfrac{1}{k}$ to $\infty$, the variable $s$ passes from $1$ to $0$.

It is therefore concluded that by making the real substitution $(i)$, the differential expression *

$$\frac{dt}{\sqrt{\pm(1 \pm g^2t^2)(1 \pm h^2t^2)}}$$

may be reduced to the form

$$\pm \frac{1}{M} \frac{dv}{\sqrt{(1-v^2)(1-k^2v^2)}},$$

where the variable $v$ lies within the interval $0 \ldots 1$. Such transformations fail if the expression under the root contains only even powers of $t$, the two roots in $t^2$ being imaginary, i.e., if $R(x) = Ax^4 + 2Bx^2 + C$, where $B^2 - AC < 0$. This case is considered in Art. 34.

**Art. 5.** It is also seen that the general elliptic integral

$$\int \frac{Q(t)}{\sqrt{R(t)}}\,dt,$$

---

* For other transformations and tables, see Tannery et Molk, *Fonctions Elliptiques*, Vol. IV, p. 34; Cayley, *Elliptic Functions*, pp. 315–16; Appell et Lacour, *Fonctions Elliptiques*, pp. 240–243.

where $Q(t)$ is any rational function of $t$, and $R(t)$ is of the fourth degree in $t$, may by the real substitutions

$$t = \frac{p+q\,\tau}{1+\tau}, \quad \tau = \frac{a+bx^2}{c+dx^2},$$

be transformed into

$$\int \frac{f(x)dx}{\sqrt{(1-x^2)(1-k^2x^2)}},$$

where $f(x)$ is a rational function of $x$. The evaluation of this latter integral, see my *Elliptic Functions*, I, p. 186, may be made to depend upon that of three types of integral, viz.:

$$F(k,\ x) = \int \frac{dx}{\sqrt{(1-x^2)(1-k^2x^2)}},$$

$$E(k,\ x) = \int \frac{\sqrt{1-k^2x^2}}{\sqrt{1-x^2}}dx,$$

$$\Pi(n,\ k,\ x) = \int \frac{dx}{(1+nx^2)\sqrt{(1-x^2)(1-k^2x^2)}}.$$

Writing $x = \sin \phi$, and putting $\sqrt{1-k^2\sin^2\phi} = \Delta(k,\ \phi)$, there results the *Legendre notation* as *normal integrals* of the *first kind*

$$F(k,\ \phi) = \int_0^\phi \frac{d\phi}{\Delta(k,\ \phi)},$$

of the *second kind*,

$$E(k,\ \phi) = \int_0^\phi \Delta(k,\ \phi)d\phi,$$

and of the *third kind*,

$$\Pi(n,\ k,\ \phi) = \int_0^\phi \frac{d\phi}{(1+n\sin^2\phi)\Delta(k,\ \phi)}.$$

The modulus $k$ is omitted from the notation when no particular emphasis is put upon it.

The evaluation of these integrals is reserved for Chap. IV. However, the nature of the first two integrals may be studied by observing the graphs in the next article.

**Art. 6.** *Graphs of the integrals $F(k, \phi)$ and $E(k, \phi)$.* In Fig. 1 there are traced the curves $y = \dfrac{1}{\Delta(k, \phi)}$ and $y = \Delta(k, \phi)$. Let values of $\phi$ be laid off upon the $X$-axis. It is seen that the areas of these curves included between the $x$-axis and the ordinates corresponding to the abscissa $\phi$ will represent the integrals $F(k, \phi)$ and $E(k, \phi)$. See Cayley, *Elliptic Functions*, p. 41.

If $k = 0$, then $\Delta\phi = 1$, and the curves $y = \Delta\phi$, $y = \dfrac{1}{\Delta\phi}$ each become the straight line $y = 1$; while the corresponding integrals

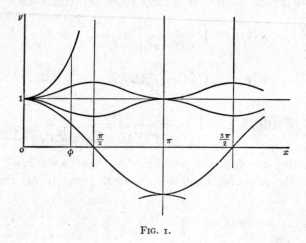

Fig. 1.

$F(\phi)$, $E(\phi)$ are both equal to $\phi$ and are represented by rectangles upon the sides $\phi$ and $1$. When $0 < k < 1$, the curve $y = \dfrac{1}{\Delta\phi}$ lies entirely above the line $y = 1$, while $y = \Delta\phi$ lies below it. As $\phi$ increases from zero, the integrals $F(\phi)$ and $E(\phi)$ increase from zero in a continuous manner, the integral $F(\phi)$ being always the larger. Further, for a given value of $\phi$, as $k$ increases the integral $F(\phi)$ increases and $E(\phi)$ diminishes; and conversely as $k$ decreases, $F(\phi)$ diminishes and $E(\phi)$ increases.

If $F\left(k, \dfrac{\pi}{2}\right)$ be denoted by $F_1(k)$, or $F_1$, and if we put

$E_1 = E\left(k, \dfrac{\pi}{2}\right)$, it is seen that when $k = 0$, $F\left(0, \dfrac{\pi}{2}\right) = F_1(0) = \dfrac{\pi}{2}$ $= E_1(0)$. When $k$ has a fixed value, it is often omitted in the notation. $F_1$ and $E_1$ are called *complete* integrals.

It is evident that both curves are symmetric about the line $y = \frac{1}{2}\pi$ and that for a fixed value of $k$, it is sufficient to

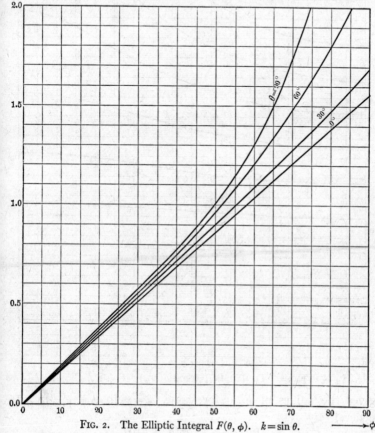

FIG. 2. The Elliptic Integral $F(\theta, \phi)$. $k = \sin \theta$. $\longrightarrow \phi$

know the values of $\phi$ from $0$ to $\frac{1}{2}\pi$. For $F(\pi) = 2F_1$, and for any value $\phi = \alpha$, $F(\alpha) = F(\pi) - F(\pi - \alpha)$, or $F(\pi - \alpha) = 2F_1 - F(\alpha)$. In the latter formula, as $\alpha$ diminishes from $\dfrac{\pi}{2}$ to $0$, $F(\phi)$ increases from $\dfrac{\pi}{2}$ to $\pi$.

Further noting that $F(-\alpha) = -F(\alpha)$, the formula

$$F(\alpha) = F(\pi) + F(\alpha - \pi),$$

$$= 2F_1 + F(\alpha - \pi),$$

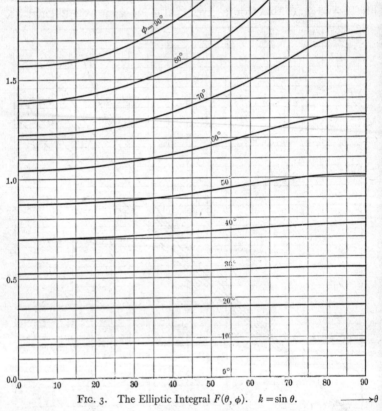

FIG. 3.   The Elliptic Integral $F(\theta, \phi)$.   $k = \sin\theta$.   $\longrightarrow \theta$

gives the values of $F(\phi)$ for values $\phi = \pi$ to $\phi = 2\pi$, etc. In general,

$$F(m\pi \pm \alpha) = 2mF_1 \pm F(\alpha),$$

$$E(m\pi \pm \alpha) = 2mE_1 \pm E(\alpha).$$

**Art. 7.** When $k = 1$, the graphs of the two curves in Fig. 1 are entirely changed, the curve $y = \Delta\phi$ becoming $y = \cos\phi$, which as before lies wholly below the line $y = 1$. The curve $y = \dfrac{1}{\Delta\phi}$

becomes $y = \sec \phi$. The ordinate for this latter curve becomes infinite for $\phi = \frac{1}{2}\pi$, and between the values $\frac{1}{2}\pi$ and $\frac{3}{2}\pi$ there is a branch lying wholly below the line $y = -1$, the ordinates for the values $\phi = \frac{1}{2}\pi$ and $\phi = \frac{3}{2}\pi$ being $= -\infty$.

For the values $\frac{3}{2}\pi$ and $\frac{5}{2}\pi$ there is a branch lying wholly

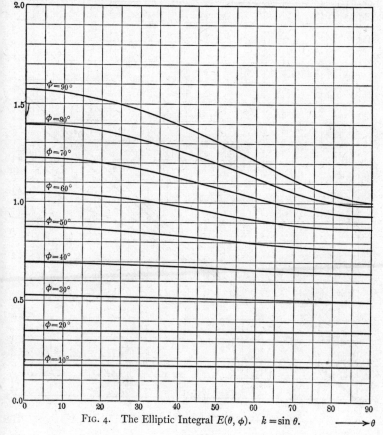

FIG. 4.   The Elliptic Integral $E(\theta, \phi)$.   $k = \sin \theta$. $\longrightarrow \theta$

above the line $y = +1$, the ordinates for $\frac{3}{2}\pi$ and $\frac{5}{2}\pi$ being $+\infty$ and so on.

Corresponding to the first curve, $E(\phi) = \int_0^\phi \cos \phi \, d\phi = \sin \phi$ and consequently $E_1 = 1$. This, taken in connection with what was given above, shows that as $k$ increases from 0 to 1, $E_1$ decreases from $\frac{1}{2}\pi$ to 1.

For the second curve, $F(\phi) = \int_0^\phi \sec\phi \, d\phi = \log\tan\left(\dfrac{\pi}{4} + \dfrac{\phi}{2}\right)$,

so that $F_1$ is logarithmically infinite when $k = 1$; and this taken in connection with what was given above, shows that

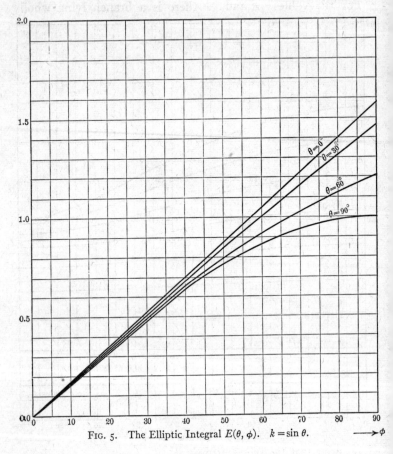

FIG. 5.    The Elliptic Integral $E(\theta, \phi)$.    $k = \sin\theta$.      $\longrightarrow \phi$

as $k$ increases from 0 to 1, $F_1$ increases from $\frac{1}{2}\pi$ to logarithmic infinity.

**Art. 8.** In Figs. 2–5 are added other graphs of the integrals $F(k, \phi)$ and $E(k, \phi)$ which require no further explanation. At the end of the book are found tables which give the values of these integrals for fixed values of $k$ and $\phi$.

## EXAMPLES

1. A quartic function with real coefficients is always equal to the product of two factors $M = l + 2mx + nx^2$, $N = \lambda + 2\mu x + \nu x^2$, where all the coefficients are real. Remove the coefficient of $x$ in $M$ and $N$ in the integral

$$\int \frac{dx}{\sqrt{MN}},$$

and thereby reduce this integral to

$$\int \frac{(q-p)dy}{\sqrt{(ay^2+b)(a'y^2+b')}},$$

by a substitution $x = \dfrac{p+qy}{1+y}$, and show that $p$ and $q$ are real. *Legendre*, Vol. I., Chap. II.

2. Show that

$$\int \frac{f(x)dx}{\sqrt{S(x)}}$$

may be reduced to the integral

$$\int \frac{g(z)dz}{\sqrt{4z^3 - g_2 z - g_3}},$$

where $f$ and $g$ are rational functions of their arguments and

$$S(x) = ax^3 + 3bx^2 + 3cx + d.$$

The substitution required is $x = mz + n$, where $n = -\dfrac{b}{a}$, $am^3 = 4$.

*Appell et Lacour*, p. 247.

3. Knowing a real root $\alpha$ of $R(x)$, find the form of $\dfrac{dx}{\sqrt{R(x)}}$, when $x = \alpha + \dfrac{1}{y}$.

Write $\qquad R(x) = (x - \alpha)(cx^3 + c_1 x^2 + c_2 x + c_3).$ *Levy*, p. 77.

4. Show that the substitution

$$\sqrt{c}\,x = \frac{(1 + \sin\phi) + \sqrt{c}(1 - \sin\phi)}{(1 - \sin\phi) + \sqrt{c}(1 + \sin\phi)}$$

transforms

$$\frac{dx}{\sqrt{(x^2-1)(1-c^2x^2)}} \quad \text{into} \quad \frac{(1+\sqrt{k})^2 d\phi}{2\sqrt{1 - k^2 \sin^2\phi}},$$

where

$$k = \left(\frac{1-\sqrt{c}}{1+\sqrt{c}}\right)^2.$$

5. Show that by the substitution $x = \dfrac{1-y}{1+y}\sqrt{\dfrac{\lambda}{\mu}}$, the integral in which $R(x)$ has the form $\lambda^2 + 2\lambda\mu \cos\theta\, x^2 + \mu^2 x^4$, is transformed into one which has under the radical an expression of the form $m^2(1+g^2y^2)(1+h^2y^2)$.

*Legendre*, Vol. I, Chap. XI.

6. If the four roots of $X$ are all real, such that $a > \beta > \gamma > \delta$, show that the substitution

$$x = \frac{\gamma(\beta-\delta) - \delta(\beta-\gamma)\,\sin^2\phi}{(\beta-\delta) - (\beta-\gamma)\,\sin^2\phi}$$

transforms

$$\frac{dx}{\sqrt{X}} \quad \text{into} \quad \frac{2}{\sqrt{(\alpha-\gamma)(\beta-\delta)}}\,\frac{d\phi}{\sqrt{1-k^2\sin^2\phi}},$$

where

$$k^2 = \frac{\beta-\gamma}{\alpha-\gamma}\frac{\alpha-\delta}{\beta-\delta} \quad \text{and} \quad \gamma < x < \beta.$$

7. If $Y$ is of the third degree and if its roots $\alpha$, $\beta$, $\gamma$ are all real, such that $a > \beta > \gamma$, show that the substitution $y = \gamma + (\beta-\gamma)\sin^2\phi$ transforms

$$\frac{dy}{\sqrt{Y}} \quad \text{into} \quad \frac{2}{\sqrt{\alpha-\gamma}}\,\frac{d\phi}{\sqrt{1-k^2\sin^2\phi}},$$

where

$$k^2 = \frac{\beta-\gamma}{\alpha-\gamma} \quad \text{and} \quad \gamma < y < \beta.$$

8. If $X$ is of the fourth degree with roots $\alpha$, $\beta$, real and $\gamma$, $\delta = \rho \pm i\sigma$, and if $M^2 = (\rho-\alpha)^2 + \sigma^2$, $N^2 = (\rho-\beta)^2 + \sigma^2$, show that the substitution

$$\frac{x-\alpha}{x-\beta} = \frac{M}{N}\frac{1-\cos\phi}{1+\cos\phi}$$

transforms

$$\frac{dx}{\sqrt{(x-\alpha)(x-\beta)[(x-\rho)^2+\sigma^2]}} \quad \text{into} \quad \frac{1}{\sqrt{MN}}\,\frac{d\phi}{\sqrt{1-k^2\sin^2\phi}},$$

where

$$k^2 = \frac{1}{2}\frac{(M+N)^2-(\alpha-\beta)^2}{2MN}$$

and

$$\infty > x > \alpha \quad \text{or} \quad \beta > x > -\infty.$$

9. Show that the substitution

$$t = e_1 + \frac{(e_2 - e_1)(e_3 - e_1)}{s - e_1}$$

transforms the integral

$$\int \frac{dt}{\sqrt{(t - e_1)(t - e_2)(t - e_3)}}$$

into itself.

10. Show that the substitutions

$$t = \frac{z - a_1}{z - a_2} \cdot \frac{a_2 - a_4}{a_2 - a_1}, \quad k^2 = \frac{a_3 - a_4}{a_3 - a_1} \cdot \frac{a_2 - a_1}{a_2 - a_4};$$

transform

$$\int_0^t \frac{dt}{\sqrt{t(1 - t)(1 - k^2 t)}} \text{ into}$$

$$\pm \sqrt{(a_4 - a_2)(a_1 - a_3)} \int_{a_1}^z \frac{dz}{\sqrt{(z - a_1)(z - a_2)(z - a_3)(z - a_4)}}.$$

11. Prove that the substitution

$$\frac{z - a_1}{z - a_2} : \frac{a_3 - a_1}{a_3 - a_2} = \frac{t - a_2}{t - a_1} : \frac{a_4 - a_2}{a_4 - a_1}$$

transforms

$$\int \frac{dz}{\sqrt{A(z - a_1)(z - a_2)(z - a_3)(z - a_4)}} \text{ into } \int \frac{dt}{\sqrt{A(t - a_1)(t - a_2)(t - a_3)(t - a_4)}}.$$

# CHAPTER II

## THE ELLIPTIC FUNCTIONS

**Art. 9.** The expressions $F(k, \phi)$, $E(k, \phi)$, $\Pi(n, k, \phi)$ were called by Legendre *elliptic functions;* these quantities are, however, *elliptic integrals.* It was Abel [*] who, about 1823, pointed out that if one studied the integral $u$ as a function of $x$ in

$$u = \int_0^x \frac{dx}{\sqrt{(1-x^2)(1-k^2x^2)}} = \int_0^\phi \frac{d\phi}{\sqrt{1-k^2 \sin^2 \phi}}, \ x = \sin \phi, \quad (1)$$

the same difficulty was met, as if he were to study the trigonometric and logarithmic functions by considering $u$ as a function of $x$ in

$$u = \int^x \frac{dx}{\sqrt{1-x^2}} = \sin^{-1} x, \text{ or } u = \int_1^x \frac{dx}{x} = \log x.$$

Abel proposed instead to study the upper limit $x$ as a function of $u$. Jacobi (*Fundamenta Nova*, § 17) introduced the notation $\phi = amplitude$ of $u$, and written $\phi = am\, u$. Considered as a function of $u$, we have $x = \sin \phi = \sin am\, u$, and associated with this function are the two other elliptic functions $\cos \phi = \cos am\, u$ and $\Delta\phi = \Delta\, am\, u = \sqrt{1 - k^2 \sin^2 \phi}$. Gudermann (teacher of Weierstrass) in *Crelle's Journal*, Bd. 18, p. 12, proposed to abbreviate this notation and to write

$$x = \sin \phi = sn\, u,$$

$$\sqrt{1-x^2} = \cos \phi = cn\, u,$$

$$\sqrt{1-k^2x^2} = \Delta\phi = dn\, u,$$

* Abel (Œuvres, Sylow and Lie edition, T. I., p. 263 and p. 518, 1827-30).

It follows at once that

$$sn^2u + cn^2u = 1,$$

$$dn^2u + k^2sn^2u = 1.$$

From (1) results $\dfrac{du}{d\phi} = \dfrac{1}{\Delta\phi}$ or $\dfrac{d\phi}{du} = \Delta\phi$, so that $\dfrac{d}{du}amu = \Delta am u = dnu$.

It is also evident that

$$\frac{d}{du}sn\,u = \frac{d}{du}\sin\phi = \cos\phi\,\frac{d\phi}{du} = cn\,u\,dn\,u,$$

$$\frac{d}{du}cn\,u = -sn\,u\,dn\,u,$$

$$\frac{d}{du}dn\,u = -k^2sn\,u\,cn\,u.$$

Further, if $u = 0$, then the upper limit $\phi = 0$, so that $am\,0 = 0$, and consequently, $sn\,0 = 0$, $cn\,0 = 1$, $dn\,0 = 1$.

If $\phi$ be changed into $-\phi$, it is seen that $u$ changes its sign, so that $am(-u) = -am\,u$, and

$$sn(-u) = -sn\,u, \quad cn(-u) = cn\,u, \quad dn(-u) = dn\,u.$$

**Art. 10.** In the theory of circular functions there is found the numerical transcendent $\pi$, a quantity such that $\sin\dfrac{\pi}{2} = 1$, $\cos\dfrac{\pi}{2} = 0$. Writing

$$u = \int_0^x \frac{dx}{\sqrt{1-x^2}} = \sin^{-1}x,$$

we have $x = \sin u$. Thus $\dfrac{\pi}{2}$ may be defined as the complete integral

$$\frac{\pi}{2} = \int_0^1 \frac{dx}{\sqrt{1-x^2}}.$$

Similarly a real positive quantity $K$ (Jacobi) may be defined through

$$K = \int_0^1 \frac{dx}{\sqrt{(1-x^2)(1-k^2x^2)}} = \int_0^{\frac{\pi}{2}} \frac{d\phi}{\sqrt{1-k^2\sin^2\phi}} = F\left(k, \frac{\pi}{2}\right)$$

(Art. 6).

Associated with $K$ is the transcendental quantity $K'$, which is the same function of the complementary modulus $k'$ as $K$ is of $k$. The transcendental nature of these two functions of $k$ and $k'$ may be observed by considering the following infinite series through which they are expressed.

If $(1-k^2\sin^2\phi)^{-\frac{1}{2}}$ be expanded in a series, then

$$F(k, \phi) = \int_0^\phi \frac{d\phi}{\sqrt{1-k^2\sin^2\phi}}$$
$$= \phi + \tfrac{1}{2}k^2v_2 + \ldots + \frac{1.3.\ \cdots\ (2n-1)}{2.4.\ \cdots\ 2n}k^{2n}\,v_{2n} + \ldots,$$

where $v_{2n} = \int_0^\phi \sin^{2n}\phi\ d\phi$.

In particular, if $\phi = \frac{\pi}{2}$, we have by Wallis's Theorem,

$$\int_0^{\frac{\pi}{2}} \sin^{2n}\phi\, d\phi = \frac{1.3.\ \cdots\ 2n-1}{2.4.\ \cdots\ 2n}\frac{\pi}{2}.$$

It follows that

$$\frac{2}{\pi}K = 1 + \left(\frac{1}{2}\right)^2 k^2 + \left(\frac{1.3}{2.4}\right)^2 k^4 + \left(\frac{1.3.5}{2.4.6}\right)^2 k^6 + \ldots$$

Similarly, it may be proved that

$$\frac{2}{\pi}E\left(k, \frac{\pi}{2}\right) = 1 - \left(\frac{1}{2}\right)^2 k^2 - \left(\frac{1.3}{2.4}\right)^2 \frac{k^4}{3} - \left(\frac{1.3.5}{2.4.6}\right)\frac{k^6}{5} - \ldots$$

which confirm the results of Arts. 6 and 7.

**Art. 11.** If in the integal $\int_{\frac{2n-1}{2}\pi}^{n\pi} \frac{d\phi}{\Delta\phi}$ there be put $\phi = n\pi - \theta$, then it becomes

$$\int_0^{\frac{\pi}{2}} \frac{d\theta}{\Delta\theta} = K; \text{ and if in the integral } \int_{n\pi}^{\frac{2n+1}{2}\pi} \frac{d\phi}{\Delta\phi}$$

we put $\phi = n\pi + \theta$, then this integral is

$$\int_0^{\frac{\pi}{2}} \frac{d\theta}{\Delta\theta} = K.$$

It follows that

$$\int_0^{n\frac{\pi}{2}} \frac{d\phi}{\Delta\phi} = \int_0^{\frac{\pi}{2}} \frac{d\phi}{\Delta\phi} + \int_{\frac{\pi}{2}}^{\pi} \frac{d\phi}{\Delta\phi} + \ldots + \int_{(n-1)\frac{\pi}{2}}^{n\frac{\pi}{2}} \frac{d\phi}{\Delta\phi} = nK,$$

so that $\frac{n\pi}{2} = am\, nK$; or, since $\frac{\pi}{2} = am\, K$, we have $am\, nK = n\, am\, K$.

Note that

$$\int_0^{n\pi+\beta} \frac{d\phi}{\Delta\phi} = \int_0^{n\pi} \frac{d\phi}{\Delta\phi} + \int_{n\pi}^{n\pi+\beta} \frac{d\phi}{\Delta\phi} = 2nK + u,$$

where

$$u = \int_{n\pi}^{n\pi+\beta} \frac{d\phi}{\Delta\phi} = \int_0^{\beta} \frac{d\theta}{\Delta\theta};$$

further, since any arc $\alpha$ may be put $= n\pi \pm \beta$, where $\beta$ is an arc between $0$ and $\frac{\pi}{2}$, we may always write

$$\alpha = n\pi \pm \beta = am(2nK \pm u),$$

or

$$2n\, am\, K \pm am\, u = am(2nK \pm u).$$

**Art. 12.** Making use of the formula just written, it is seen that $am\, K = \frac{\pi}{2}$,

$$sn\, K = 1, \quad cn\, K = 0, \quad dn\, K = k'.$$

$$sn(u \pm 2K) = -sn\, u, \quad cn(u \pm 2K) = -cn\, u, \quad dn(u \pm 2K) = dn\, u;$$

$$sn(u \pm 4K) = sn\, u, \quad cn(u \pm 4K) = cn\, u, \quad dn(u \pm 4K) = dn\, u.$$

Note that $4K$ is a *period* of the three elliptic transcendents $sn\, u$, $cn\, u$ and $dn\, u$; in fact, it is seen that $2K$ is a period of $dn\, u$ and of $\frac{sn\, u}{cn\, u} = tn\, u$. Also note that

$$sn\, 2K = 0, \quad cn\, 2K = -1, \quad dn\, 2K = 1,$$
$$sn\, 4K = 0, \quad cn\, 4K = 1, \qquad dn\, 4K = 1.$$

Of course, the modulus of the above functions is $k$; and, since $K'$ is the same function of $k'$ as $K$ is of $k$, we also have

$$sn(u \pm 2K', k') = -sn(u, k'),$$
$$sn(u \pm 4K', k') = sn(u, k'), \text{ etc.}$$

**Art. 13.** *The Gudermannian.* As introductory to the Jacobi imaginary transformation of the following article, there is a particular case * where $k = 1$. Then

$$u = F(1, \phi) = \int_0^\phi \frac{d\phi}{\sqrt{1 - \sin^2 \phi}} = \log \tan \left( \frac{\pi}{4} + \frac{\phi}{2} \right). \quad \text{(Cf. Art. 7.)}$$

Here $\phi$, considered as a function of $u$, may be called the Gudermannian and written $\phi = gd\, u$, the functions corresponding to $sn\, u$ and $cn\, u$ being $sg\, u$ and $cg\, u$. Then

$$e^u = \tan \left( \frac{\pi}{4} + \frac{\phi}{2} \right) = \frac{1 + \tan \phi/2}{1 - \tan \phi/2} = \frac{1 + \sin \phi}{\cos \phi} = \frac{\cos \phi}{1 - \sin \phi};$$

or,

$$e^u = \frac{1 + sg\, u}{cg\, u}, \quad e^{-u} = \frac{cg\, u}{1 + sg\, u} = \frac{1 - sg\, u}{cg\, u}.$$

It follows that

$$cg\, u = \frac{2}{e^u + e^{-u}} = \frac{1}{\cos iu} = \frac{1}{\cosh u} = \text{sech}\, u,$$

and

$$sg\, u = \frac{e^u - e^{-u}}{e^u + e^{-u}} = -i \frac{\sin iu}{\cos iu} = \frac{\sinh u}{\cosh u} = \tanh u.$$

These formulas may be written

| | |
|---|---|
| $sg\, u = -i \tan iu,$ | $\sin iu = i\, tg\, u,$ |
| $cg\, u = 1/\cos iu,$ | $\cos iu = 1/cg\, u,$ |
| $tg\, u = -i \sin iu;$ | $\tan iu = i\, sg\, u.$ |

* See Gudermann, *Crelle*, Bd. 18, pp. 1, et seq.; see also Cayley, loc. cit. p. 56; Weierstrass, Math. Werke I, pp. 1–49 and the remark p. 50.

The above relations may also be derived by considering two angles $\theta$ and $\phi$ connected by the equation $\cos \theta \cos \phi = 1$. For there follows at once

$$\begin{array}{l|l} \sin \theta = i \tan \phi, & \sin \phi = -i \tan \theta, \\ \cos \theta = 1/\cos \phi, & \cos \phi = 1/\cos \theta, \\ \tan \theta = i \sin \phi, & \tan \phi = -i \sin \theta. \end{array}$$

Further, there results,

$$\cos \theta \, d\theta = i \sec^2 \phi \, d\phi, \quad \text{or} \quad d\theta = i \frac{d\phi}{\cos \phi}.$$

It follows that

$$\theta = i \log \tan \left( \frac{\pi}{4} + \frac{\phi}{2} \right).$$

Then, by assuming that $\phi = gd\, u$, we have $\theta = iu$, and consequently the foregoing relations.

**Art. 14.** *Jacobi's Imaginary Transformations.*[*] Writing

$$\sin \theta = i \tan \phi, \ \cos \theta = \frac{1}{\cos \phi}, \ \sin \phi = -i \tan \theta, \ \Delta(\theta, k) = \frac{\Delta(\phi, k')}{\cos \phi},$$

we have $d\theta = i \dfrac{d\phi}{\cos \phi}$ and $\displaystyle\int_0^\theta \frac{d\theta}{\Delta(\theta, k)} = i \int_0^\phi \frac{d\phi}{\Delta(\phi, k')}.$

If, then, $\displaystyle\int_0^\phi \frac{d\phi}{\Delta(\phi, k')} = u$, so that $\phi = am(u, k')$, there results $\displaystyle\int_0^\theta \frac{d\theta}{\Delta(\theta, k)} = iu$, and $\theta = am\, iu$.

These expressions, substituted in the above relations, give

$$sn(iu, k) = i \, tn(u, k'),$$

$$cn(iu, k) = \frac{1}{cn(u, k')},$$

$$dn(iu, k) = \frac{dn(u, k')}{cn(u, k')}.$$

From this it is evident that the two functions *cn* and *dn* have real values for imaginary values of the argument, while $sn(iu)$ is an imaginary quantity.

[*] Jacobi, *Fundamenta Nova*, § 19. See also Abel, *Œuvres*, T. I., p. 272.

Among the trigonometric and exponential functions, we have, for example, the relation

$$\cos iu = \frac{e^u + e^{-u}}{2},$$

where the argument of the trigonometric function is real while that of the exponential function is real. We note that an elliptic function with imaginary argument may be expressed through an elliptic function with real argument, whose modulus is the complement of the original modulus.

**Art. 15.** From the formulas of the preceding article it follows at once

$$sn[i(u+4K'), k] = i\, tn(u+4K', k') = sn(iu, k),$$

and also

$$cn(iu+4iK', k) = cn(iu, k),$$

$$dn(iu+4iK', k) = dn(iu, k).$$

If in these formulas $iu$ be changed into $u$, we have

$$sn(u\pm 4iK', k) = sn(u, k),$$

$$cn(u\pm 4iK', k) = cn(u, k),$$

$$dn(u\pm 4iK', k) = dn(u, k).$$

It also follows that $sn(u\pm 4iK, k') = sn(u, k')$, etc. If in the formula $sn(iu) = i\, tn(u, k')$, we put $u+2K'$ in the place of $u$, then

$$sn(iu+2iK', k) = i\, tn(u+2K', k') = i\, tn(u, k') = sn\, iu.$$

Changing $iu$ to $u$, we have

$$sn(u\pm 2iK') = sn\, u, \quad cn(u\pm 2iK') = -cn\, u, \quad dn(u\pm 2iK') = -dn\, u,$$

and

$$sn(2iK') = 0, \quad cn(2iK') = -1, \quad dn(2iK') = -1.$$

The modulus $k$ is always understood, unless another modulus is indicated.

It follows at once that

$$sn(u\pm4iK') = sn\,u, \quad cn(u\pm4iK') = cn\,u, \quad dn(u\pm4iK') = dn\,u,$$

and

$$sn(4iK') = 0, \qquad cn(4iK') = 1, \qquad dn(4iK') = 1.$$

It is also seen that

$$sn(u\pm2K\pm2iK') = -sn\,u,$$
$$sn(u\pm4K\pm4iK') = sn\,u, \text{ etc.}$$

In particular, notice that

the periods of $sn\,u$ are $4K$ and $2iK'$,
the periods of $cn\,u$ are $4K$ and $2K+2iK'$,
the periods of $dn\,u$ are $2K$ and $4iK'$.

**Art. 16.** *Periodic Functions.* Consider the simple case of the exponential function $e^u$ and suppose that $u = x+iy$. It may be shown that $e^{u+2\pi i} = e^u$ for all values of $u$; for it is seen that $e^u = e^{x+iy} = e^x(\cos y + i \sin y)$. If we increase $u$ by $2\pi i$, then $y$ is increased by $2\pi$ and consequently

$$e^{u+2\pi i} = e^x[\cos(y+2\pi) + i\sin(y+2\pi)] = e^x(\cos y + i\sin y) = e^u.$$

It follows that if it is desired to examine the function $e^u$, then clearly this function need not be studied in the whole $u$-plane, but only within a strip which lies above the $X$-axis and has the breadth $2\pi$; for we see at once that to every point $u_0$ which lies without this *period-strip* there corresponds a point $u_1$ within the strip and in such a way that the function has the same value and the same properties at $u_0$ and $u_1$.

Similarly it is seen that the two functions $\sin u$ and $\cos u$ have the real period $2\pi$, and consequently it is necessary to study these functions only within a period-strip which lies adjacent to the $Y$-axis with a breadth $2\pi$. As already noted, Abel and Jacobi found that the elliptic functions had two periods. In the preceding article it was seen that $sn\,u$ had the real period $4K$ and the imaginary period $2iK'$.

On the $X$-axis lay off a distance $4K$ and on the $Y$-axis a distance $2K'$ and construct the rectangle on these two sides. Further suppose that the whole plane is filled out with such rectangles.

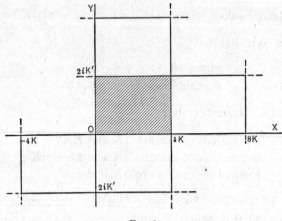

Fig. 6.

Then it will be seen that the function $sn\,u$ behaves in every rectangle precisely as it does in the initial rectangle. Similar parallelograms may be constructed for the functions $cn\,u$ and $dn\,u$. See Art. 21.

**Art. 17.** Next write $\sin\phi = \dfrac{\cos\theta}{\Delta\theta}$, so that $\cos\phi = \dfrac{k'\sin\theta}{\Delta\theta}$, and $\Delta\phi = \dfrac{k'}{\Delta\theta}$. It follows that $\dfrac{d\phi}{\Delta\phi} = -\dfrac{d\theta}{\Delta\theta}$ and consequently

$$\int_0^\phi \frac{d\phi}{\Delta\phi} = \int_\theta^{\frac{\pi}{2}} \frac{d\theta}{\Delta\theta} = \int_0^{\frac{\pi}{2}} \frac{d\theta}{\Delta\theta} - \int_0^\theta \frac{d\theta}{\Delta\theta} = K - u,$$

if we put $u = \displaystyle\int_0^\theta \frac{d\theta}{\Delta\theta}$, or $\theta = am\,u$. It follows that $\phi = am(K-u)$, and from the above formulas

$$sn(K-u) = \frac{cn\,u}{dn\,u}, \quad cn(K-u) = \frac{k'\,sn\,u}{dn\,u}, \quad dn(K-u) = \frac{k'}{dn\,u}.$$

In these formulas change $-u$ to $u$ and note that $sn(-u) = -sn\,u$, etc.

It is seen that

$$sn(u \pm K) = \pm \frac{cn\,u}{dn\,u} \qquad sn\,K = 1,$$

$$cn(u \pm K) = \mp \frac{k'sn\,u}{dn\,u}, \qquad cn\,K = 0,$$

$$dn(u \pm K) = + \frac{k'}{dn\,u}, \qquad dn\,K = k'.$$

For the calculation of the elliptic functions, the above relations permit the reduction of the argument so that it is always comprised between 0 and $\frac{1}{2}K$, just as in trigonometry the angle may be reduced so as to lie between 0 and $45°$ for the calculation of the circular functions.

**Art. 18.** In the above formulas put $iu$ in the place of $u$, and it is seen that

$$sn(iu \pm K) = \pm \frac{cn\,iu}{dn\,iu} = \pm \frac{1}{dn(u,\,k')},$$

$$cn(iu \pm K) = \mp \frac{ik'sn(u,\,k')}{dn(u,\,k')},$$

$$dn(iu \pm K) = \frac{k'cn(u,\,k')}{dn(u,\,k')}.$$

Further, in the formulas $sn\,iu = i\,tn(u,\,k')$, etc., write $u \pm iK$ for $u$ and it is seen that

$$sn(iu \pm iK',\,k) = i\,tg\,am(u \pm K',\,k') = -\frac{i}{k}\frac{cn(u,\,k')}{sn(u,\,k')},$$

$$cn(iu \pm iK',\,k) = \mp \frac{dn(u,\,k')}{sn(u,\,k')},$$

$$dn(iu \pm iK',\,k) = \mp \frac{1}{sn(u,\,k')}.$$

In the above formulas change $iu$ to $u$. We then have

$$sn(u \pm iK') = \frac{1}{k}\frac{1}{sn\,u},$$

$$cn(u \pm iK') = \mp \frac{i}{k}\frac{dn\,u}{sn\,u},$$

$$dn(u \pm iK') = \mp i\,cot\,am\,u.$$

If in these formulas $u=0$, then

$$sn(\pm iK') = \infty, \quad cn(\pm iK') = \infty, \quad dn(\pm iK') = \infty.$$

Further, if in the preceding formulas $u+K$ be put in the place of $u$, then

$$sn(u+K\pm iK') = \frac{1}{k}\,\frac{1}{sn(u+K)} = \frac{1}{k}\,\frac{dn\,u}{cn\,u}$$

$$cn(u+K\pm iK') = \mp\frac{ik'}{k\,cn\,u},$$

$$dn(u+K\pm iK') = \pm ik'\,tg\,am\,u;$$

and from these formulas, writing, $u=0$, there results

$$sn(K\pm iK') = \frac{1}{k}, \quad cn(K\pm iK') = \mp\frac{ik'}{k}, \quad dn(K\pm iK') = 0.$$

**Art. 19.** Note the analogy of the transcendent $K$ of the elliptic functions to $\frac{\pi}{2}$ of the circular functions. Due to the relation $am(K-u) = \frac{\pi}{2} - am\,u$ (Art. 11) Jacobi called the amplitude of $K-u$ the *co-amplitude* of $u$ and wrote $am(K-u) = coam\,u$.

It follows at once from the above formulas that

$$\sin coam\,u = \frac{cn\,u}{dn\,u},$$

$$\cos coam\,u = \frac{k'sn\,u}{dn\,u},$$

$$\Delta\,coam\,u = \frac{k'}{dn\,u}.$$

$$\sin coam(iu, k) = \frac{1}{dn(u, k')}, \text{ etc.}$$

**Art. 20.** *Remark.* The results obtained for the imaginary argument have been derived by making use of Jacobi's imaginary transformation; and by changing $iu$ into $u$ we have implicitly made the assumption (proved in my *Elliptic Functions*, Vol. I,

Chaps **X** and **XI**) that the elliptic functions have the same properties for real and imaginary arguments.

Art. 21. By a *zero* of a function, *sn u* for example, we mean that value of *u* which, when substituted for *u* in *sn u*, causes this function to be zero, while an *infinity* of a function is a value of *u* which causes the function to become infinite.

In studying the following graphs note that on the boundaries of the period parallelogram of *sn u*, there are six points at which this function becomes zero; but if the adjacent period parallelograms be constructed, it will be seen that only *two* zeros belong to each parallelogram. In fact, in each period-parallelogram there are *two* values of *u* which cause the function to take any fixed value; that is, any value being fixed, there are always two values of *u* which cause the function to take this value. From the following graphs it is seen that any *real* value situated within the interval $-\infty$ to $+\infty$ is taken twice by each of the three functions *sn u, cn u, dn u*.

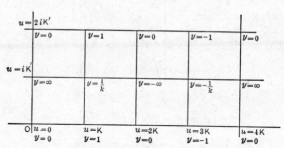

FIG. 7. $y = \operatorname{sn}(u, k)$.

ZEROS INFINITIES

$$2mK + 2niK' \qquad 2mK + (2n+1)iK'$$

where *m* and *n* are any integers.

PERIODS

$$4K,\ 2iK'$$

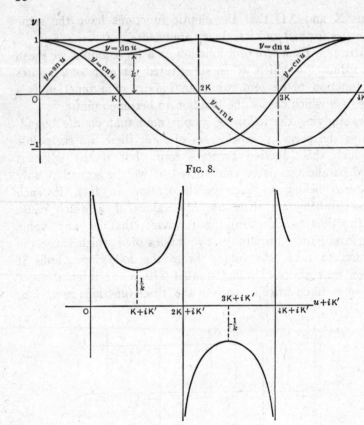

FIG. 8.

FIG. 9.   $y = \mathrm{sn}(u + iK')$.

In Fig. 9, the value $iK'$ coincides with the origin.

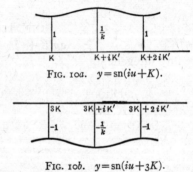

FIG. 10a.   $y = \mathrm{sn}(iu + K)$.

FIG. 10b.   $y = \mathrm{sn}(iu + 3K)$.

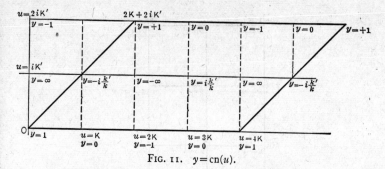

FIG. 11.   $y = \operatorname{cn}(u)$.

ZEROS

$(2m+1)K + 2niK'$

INFINITIES

$2mK + (2n+1)iK'$

where $m$ and $n$ are any integers.

PERIODS

$4K,\; 2K + 2iK'$

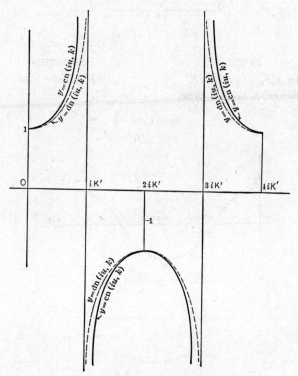

FIG. 12.   $y = \operatorname{cn}(iu)$;   $y = \operatorname{dn}(iu)$.

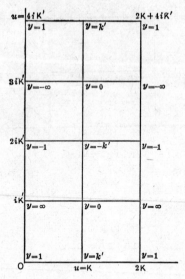

FIG. 13.   $y = \mathrm{dn}(u)$.

| ZEROS | INFINITIES |
|---|---|
| $(2m+1)K + (2n+1)iK'$ | $2mK + (2n+1)iK'$ |

where $m$ and $n$ are integers.

PERIODS

$2K, \; 4iK'$

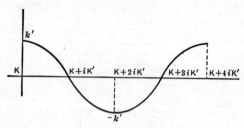

FIG. 14.   $y = \mathrm{dn}(K + iu)$.

## EXAMPLES

1. In the formulas of Art. 17 put $u=\dfrac{K}{2}$, and show first that $dn\dfrac{K}{2}=\sqrt{k'}$
and then $sn^2\dfrac{K}{2}=\dfrac{1-k'}{k^2}=\dfrac{1}{1+k'}$, $cn^2\dfrac{K}{2}=\dfrac{k'}{1+k'}$, $am\dfrac{K}{2}=\tan^{-1}\sqrt{\dfrac{1}{k'}}$.

2. Prove that
$$sn\tfrac{3}{2}K=\frac{1}{\sqrt{1+k'}}, \quad cn\tfrac{3}{2}K=-\frac{\sqrt{k'}}{\sqrt{1+k'}}, \quad dn\tfrac{3}{2}K=\sqrt{k'}.$$

3. Prove that
$$sn\frac{iK'}{2}=\frac{i}{\sqrt{k}}, \quad cn\frac{iK'}{2}=\frac{\sqrt{1+k}}{\sqrt{k}}, \quad dn\frac{iK'}{2}=\sqrt{1+k}.$$

4. Show that
$$sn(K+\tfrac{1}{2}iK')=\frac{1}{\sqrt{k}}, \quad cn(K+\tfrac{1}{2}iK')=-i\frac{\sqrt{1-k}}{\sqrt{k}}, \quad dn(K+\tfrac{1}{2}iK')=\sqrt{1-k}.$$

5. Show that
$$sn(\tfrac{1}{2}K+\tfrac{1}{2}iK')=\frac{1}{\sqrt{2k}}\big[\sqrt{1+k}+i\sqrt{1-k}\,\big],$$

$$cn(\tfrac{3}{2}K+\tfrac{1}{2}iK')=-\frac{1+i\sqrt{k'}}{\sqrt{2k}},$$

$$dn(\tfrac{1}{2}K+\tfrac{3}{2}iK')=-\frac{\sqrt{k'}}{2}\big(\sqrt{1+k'}+i\sqrt{1-k'}\,\big).$$

6. Show that
$$sn(u+K+3iK')=\frac{dn\,u}{k\,cn\,u},$$

$$cn(u+3K+iK')=\frac{ik'}{kcn\,u},$$

$$dn(u+3K+3iK')=\frac{-k'sn\,u}{cn\,u}.$$

7. Making the linear transformation $x=kz$, we have
$$\int_0^x \frac{dx}{\sqrt{\left(1-x^2\right)\left(1-\dfrac{x^2}{k^2}\right)}}=k\int_0^z \frac{dz}{\sqrt{(1-z^2)(1-k^2z^2)}}.$$

Further, put
$$u=\int_0^z \frac{dz}{\sqrt{(1-z^2)(1-k^2z^2)}}, \quad ku=\int_0^x \frac{dx}{\sqrt{\left(1-x^2\right)\left(1-\dfrac{x^2}{k^2}\right)}},$$

and show that

$$sn\left(ku, \frac{1}{k}\right) = k\, sn(u, k),$$

$$cn\left(ku, \frac{1}{k}\right) = dn(u, k),$$

$$dn\left(ku, \frac{1}{k}\right) = cn(u, k);$$

$$sn\left(ku, \frac{ik'}{k}\right) = cos\, coam(u, k'),$$

$$cn\left(ku, \frac{ik'}{k}\right) = sin\, coam\, (u, k'),$$

$$dn\left(ku, \frac{ik'}{k}\right) = \frac{1}{\Delta am(u, k')}.$$

8. The quadratic substitution $t = \dfrac{(1+k)z}{1+k z^2}$ transforms $\dfrac{dz}{\sqrt{(1-z^2)(1-k^2z^2)}}$

into $\dfrac{M dt}{\sqrt{(1-t^2)(1-l^2 t^2)}}$, where $l = \dfrac{2\sqrt{k}}{1+k}$ and $M = \dfrac{1}{1+k}$.

9. Show that

$$sn\left[(1+k)u, \frac{2\sqrt{k}}{1+k}\right] = \frac{(1+k)sn(u, k)}{1+k\, sn^2(u, k)},$$

$$cn\left[(1+k)u, \frac{2\sqrt{k}}{1+k}\right] = \frac{cn(u, k)dn(u, k)}{1+k\, sn^2(u, k)},$$

$$dn\left[(1+k)u, \frac{2\sqrt{k}}{1+k}\right] = \frac{1-k\, sn^2(u, k)}{1+k\, sn^2(u, k)}.$$

# CHAPTER III

## ELLIPTIC INTEGRALS OF THE FIRST KIND REDUCED TO LEGENDRE'S NORMAL FORM

**Art. 22.** In the elementary calculus such integrals as the following have been studied

$$\int_0^x \frac{dx}{\sqrt{1-x^2}} = \sin^{-1} x = \cos^{-1} \sqrt{1-x^2},$$

$$\int_x^\infty \frac{dx}{x^2+1} = \cot^{-1} x = \tan^{-1} \frac{1}{x},$$

$$\int_1^x \frac{dx}{\sqrt{x^2-1}} = \cosh^{-1} x = \sinh^{-1} \sqrt{x^2-1} = \log\{x + \sqrt{x^2-1}\}.$$

Following Clifford * an analogous notation for the elliptic integrals will be introduced. Write (see Art. 9),

$$x = sn\, u, \quad \sqrt{1-x^2} = cn\, u, \quad \sqrt{1-k^2x^2} = dn\, u.$$

Since (see Art. 9), $\dfrac{dx}{du} = cn\, u\, dn\, u$, it follows that

$$\frac{dx}{du} = \sqrt{(1-x^2)(1-k^2x^2)};$$

or

$$\int_0^x \frac{dx}{\sqrt{(1-x^2)(1-k^2x^2)}} = u = sn^{-1} x = cn^{-1} \sqrt{1-x^2} = dn^{-1}\sqrt{1-k^2x^2}$$
$$= F(k, \phi) = F(k, \sin^{-1} x). \quad . \quad . \quad . \quad (1)$$

In particular, it is seen from this formula that the substitution $x = \sin\phi$ transforms the integral $\displaystyle\int_0^x \frac{dx}{\sqrt{(1-x^2)(1-k^2x^2)}}$

---

* Clifford, *Mathematical Papers*, p. 207.

into the normal form $\int_0^\phi \dfrac{dx}{\sqrt{1-k^2\sin^2\phi}}=F(k,\phi)$. Further, from the tables given at the end of the book, which we shall learn later to construct and use, the integral is known as soon as $x$ is fixed.

Similarly, if there be put $x=cn\,u$, $\sqrt{1-x^2}=sn\,u$, $\sqrt{k'^2+k^2x^2}$
$=dn\,u$, $\dfrac{dx}{du}=\dfrac{d\,cn\,u}{du}=-sn\,u\,dn\,u=-\sqrt{(1-x^2)(k'^2+k^2x^2)}$, it follows that

$$\int_x^1 \frac{dx}{\sqrt{(1-x^2)(k'^2+k^2x^2)}}=u=cn^{-1}x=sn^{-1}\sqrt{1-x^2}=dn^{-1}\sqrt{k'^2+k^2x^2}$$

$$=F(k,\phi)=F(k,\cos^{-1}x)$$

$$=F(k,\sin^{-1}\sqrt{1-x^2}).\quad\ldots\quad\ldots\quad (2)$$

It is seen also that the substitution $x=\cos\phi$ transforms the integral on the right-hand side into the normal form.

If $x=dn\,u$, $\dfrac{\sqrt{1-x^2}}{k}=sn\,u$, $\dfrac{\sqrt{x^2-k'^2}}{k}=cn\,u$, $\dfrac{dx}{du}=-k^2sn\,u\,cn\,u$
$=-\sqrt{(1-x^2)(x^2-k'^2)}$, we have

$$\int_x^1 \frac{dx}{\sqrt{(1-x^2)(x^2-k'^2)}}=u=dn^{-1}x=sn^{-1}\left(\frac{\sqrt{1-x^2}}{k}\right)$$

$$=cn^{-1}\left(\frac{\sqrt{x^2-k'^2}}{k}\right)=F(k,\phi)$$

$$=F\left[k,\sin^{-1}\left(\frac{\sqrt{1-x^2}}{k}\right)\right].\quad\ldots\quad\ldots\quad (3)$$

Further, writing $x=\tan\,am\,u$, it follows that $sn\,u=\dfrac{x}{\sqrt{1+x^2}}$,

$cn\,u=\dfrac{1}{\sqrt{1+x^2}}$, $dn\,u=\dfrac{\sqrt{1+k'^2x^2}}{\sqrt{1+x^2}}$, $\dfrac{dx}{du}=\dfrac{dn\,u}{cn^2u}=\sqrt{(1+x^2)(1+k'^2x^2)}$,

and

$$\int_0^x \frac{dx}{\sqrt{(1+x^2)(1+k'^2x^2)}}=u=tn^{-1}x=sn^{-1}\left(\frac{x}{\sqrt{1+x^2}}\right)$$

$$=F(k,\tan^{-1}x).\quad (4)$$

**Art. 23.** 1. If $a>b>x>0$, write $x=b\sin\phi$ in the integral,

$$v=\int_0^x \frac{dx}{\sqrt{(a^2-x^2)(b^2-x^2)}},$$

and we have, if $k^2=\dfrac{b^2}{a^2}$,

$$v=\frac{1}{a}\int_0^\phi \frac{d\phi}{\sqrt{1-k^2\sin^2\phi}}=\frac{1}{a}sn^{-1}\left[\frac{x}{b},\frac{b}{a}\right]\quad . \quad . \quad . \quad (5a)$$

2. If $\infty>x>a$, write $x=\dfrac{a}{\sin\phi}$, and it is seen that

$$\int_x^\infty \frac{dx}{\sqrt{(x^2-a^2)(x^2-b^2)}}=\frac{1}{a}sn^{-1}\left[\frac{a}{x},\frac{b}{a}\right]. \quad . \quad . \quad (5b)$$

If $a>b>x>0$,

$$\int_x^b \frac{dx}{\sqrt{(a^2+x^2)(b^2-x^2)}}=\frac{1}{\sqrt{a^2+b^2}}cn^{-1}\left[\frac{x}{b},\frac{b}{\sqrt{a^2+b^2}}\right]; \quad (6a)$$

(see IV, in Art. 3), and also

$$\int_b^x \frac{dx}{\sqrt{(a^2+x^2)(x^2-b^2)}}=\frac{1}{\sqrt{a^2+b^2}}cn^{-1}\left[\frac{b}{x},\frac{a}{\sqrt{a^2+b^2}}\right], \quad (6b)$$

(see V in Art. 3).

It is almost superfluous to add that for example in $(6a)$ the substitution $\dfrac{x}{b}=\cos\phi$ transforms the integral

$$\int_x^b \frac{dx}{\sqrt{(a^2+x^2)(b^2-x^2)}}$$

into

$$\frac{1}{\sqrt{a^2+b^2}}\int_0^\phi \frac{d\phi}{\sqrt{1-\dfrac{b^2}{a^2+b^2}\sin^2\phi}}=\frac{1}{\sqrt{a^2+b^2}}F\left[\frac{b}{\sqrt{a^2+b^2}},\cos^{-1}\frac{x}{b}\right].$$

It is also seen that if $a>x>b>0$,

$$\int_x^a \frac{dx}{\sqrt{(a^2-x^2)(x^2-b^2)}}=\frac{1}{a}dn^{-1}\left[\frac{x}{a},\frac{\sqrt{a^2-b^2}}{a}\right]; \quad . \quad . \quad (7)$$

that is, the integral on the left-hand side becomes

$$\frac{1}{a}\int_0^\phi \frac{d\phi}{\sqrt{1 - \dfrac{a^2 - b^2}{a^2}\sin^2\phi}},$$

for the substitution

$$\frac{x}{a} = \sqrt{1 - \frac{a^2 - b^2}{a^2}\sin^2\phi}.$$

Further if $a > b$

$$\int_0^x \frac{dx}{\sqrt{(x^2 + a^2)(x^2 + b^2)}} = \frac{1}{a}tn^{-1}\left[\frac{x}{b},\ \sqrt{\frac{a^2 - b^2}{a^2}}\right] \quad . \quad . \quad (8)$$

(See I in Art. 3.)

**Art. 24.** In the formulas (1), (2), (3) and (4) above, substitute $x$ for $x^2$, and it is seen that

$$\int_0^x \frac{dx}{\sqrt{x(1-x)(1-k^2x)}} = 2sn^{-1}(\sqrt{x},\ k) = 2cn^{-1}(\sqrt{1-x},\ k)$$

$$= 2dn^{-1}(\sqrt{1-k^2x},\ k),\ \ .\ .\ .\ .\ (9)$$

$$\int_x^1 \frac{dx}{\sqrt{x(1-x)(k'^2+k^2x)}} = 2cn^{-1}(\sqrt{x},\ k),\ \ .\ .\ .\ .\ .\ (10)$$

$$\int_x^1 \frac{dx}{\sqrt{x(1-x)(x-k'^2)}} = 2dn^{-1}(\sqrt{x},\ k),\ \ .\ .\ .\ .\ .\ (11)$$

$$\int_0^x \frac{dx}{\sqrt{x(1+x)(1+k'^2x)}} = 2tn^{-1}(\sqrt{x},\ k)\ \ .\ .\ .\ .\ .\ (12)$$

**Art. 25.** Suppose that $\alpha$, $\beta$, and $\gamma$ are real quantities such that $\alpha > \beta > \gamma$; further write $M = \dfrac{\sqrt{\alpha-\gamma}}{2}$, $k_1^2 = \dfrac{\beta-\gamma}{\alpha-\gamma}$ and $k_2^2 = \dfrac{\alpha-\beta}{\alpha-\gamma}$, where $k_1^2 + k_2^2 = 1$, so that the one is the complementary modulus of the other. Put $X = (x-\alpha)(x-\beta)(x-\gamma)$.

If $\infty > x > \alpha > \beta > \gamma$, write $x - \gamma = (\alpha-\gamma)\operatorname{cosec}^2\phi$ and we have

$$M\int_x^\infty \frac{dx}{\sqrt{X}} = sn^{-1}\left(\sqrt{\frac{\alpha-\gamma}{x-\gamma}},\ k_1\right) = cn^{-1}\left(\sqrt{\frac{x-\alpha}{x-\gamma}},\ k_1\right). \quad (13)$$

When $\infty > x > \alpha > \beta > \gamma$, it is seen that

$$M \int_{\alpha}^{x} \frac{dx}{\sqrt{X}} = sn^{-1}\left(\sqrt{\frac{x-\alpha}{x-\beta}}, k_1\right) = cn^{-1}\left(\sqrt{\frac{\alpha-\beta}{x-\beta}}, k_1\right), \quad (14)$$

and when $\beta > x > \gamma$, we have

$$M \int_{x}^{\beta} \frac{dx}{\sqrt{X}} = sn^{-1}\left[\sqrt{\frac{(\alpha-\gamma)(\beta-x)}{(\beta-\gamma)(\alpha-x)}}, k_1\right]$$
$$= cn^{-1}\left[\sqrt{\frac{(\alpha-\beta)(x-\gamma)}{(\beta-\gamma)(\alpha-x)}}, k_1\right]. \quad (15)$$

Further if $\beta > x > \gamma$, then

$$M \int_{\gamma}^{x} \frac{dx}{\sqrt{X}} = sn^{-1}\left(\sqrt{\frac{x-\gamma}{\beta-\gamma}}, k_1\right) = cn^{-1}\left(\sqrt{\frac{\beta-x}{\beta-\gamma}}, k_1\right)$$
$$= dn^{-1}\left(\sqrt{\frac{\alpha-x}{\alpha-\gamma}}, k_1\right). \quad (16)$$

**Art. 26.** As above write

$$M = \frac{\sqrt{\alpha-\gamma}}{2}, \quad k_2^2 = \frac{\alpha-\beta}{\alpha-\gamma}, \quad X = (x-\alpha)(x-\beta)(x-\gamma).$$

For the interval $\alpha > x > \beta > \gamma$, it is seen that

$$M \int_{x}^{\alpha} \frac{dx}{\sqrt{-X}} = sn^{-1}\left[\sqrt{\frac{\alpha-x}{\alpha-\beta}}, k_2\right] = cn^{-1}\left[\sqrt{\frac{x-\beta}{\alpha-\beta}}, k_2\right], \quad (17)$$

and for the same interval

$$M \int_{\beta}^{x} \frac{dx}{\sqrt{-X}} = sn^{-1}\left[\sqrt{\frac{(\alpha-\gamma)(x-\beta)}{(\alpha-\beta)(x-\gamma)}}, k_2\right]$$
$$= cn^{-1}\left[\sqrt{\frac{(\beta-\gamma)(\alpha-x)}{(\alpha-\beta)(x-\gamma)}}, k_2\right]. \quad (18)$$

Further, if $\gamma > x > -\infty$, then

$$M \int_{x}^{\gamma} \frac{dx}{\sqrt{-X}} = sn^{-1}\left[\sqrt{\frac{\gamma-x}{\beta-x}}, k_2\right] = cn^{-1}\left[\sqrt{\frac{\beta-\gamma}{\beta-x}}, k_2\right], \quad (19)$$

and for the same interval

$$M \int_{-\infty}^{x} \frac{dx}{\sqrt{-X}} = sn^{-1}\left(\sqrt{\frac{\alpha-\gamma}{\alpha-x}}, k_2\right) = cn^{-1}\left(\sqrt{\frac{\gamma-x}{\alpha-x}}, k_2\right). \quad (20)$$

**Art. 27.** From formula (14) it is seen that, if $\infty > x > \dfrac{1}{k^2}$,

$$\int_{\frac{1}{k^2}}^{x} \frac{dx}{\sqrt{x(x-1)(k^2x-1)}} = \frac{1}{k}\int_{\frac{1}{k^2}}^{x} \frac{dx}{\sqrt{x(x-1)(x-1/k^2)}}$$

$$= 2sn^{-1}\left(\sqrt{\frac{x-1/k^2}{x-1}},\, k\right) = 2cn^{-1}\left(\sqrt{\frac{1-k^2}{k^2(x-1)}},\, k\right), \quad (21)$$

and from formula (13) for the same interval,

$$\int_{x}^{\infty} \frac{dx}{\sqrt{x(1-x)(1-k^2x)}} = 2sn^{-1}\left(\sqrt{\frac{1}{k^2x}},\, k\right) = 2cn^{-1}\left(\sqrt{\frac{k^2x-1}{k^2x}},\, k\right) \quad (22).$$

Using formula (17), it follows that, if $\dfrac{1}{k^2} > x > 1$,

$$\int_{x}^{\frac{1}{k^2}} \frac{dx}{\sqrt{x(1-x)(1-k^2x)}} = 2i\, sn^{-1}\left(\sqrt{\frac{1-k^2x}{1-k^2}},\, k'\right)$$

$$= 2i\, cn^{-1}\left(\sqrt{\frac{k^2(x-1)}{1-k^2}},\, k'\right), \quad (23)$$

and for the same interval (see formula (18)),

$$\int_{1}^{x} \frac{dx}{\sqrt{x(1-x)(1-k^2x)}} = 2i\, sn^{-1}\left(\sqrt{\frac{x-1}{x(1-k^2)}},\, k'\right)$$

$$= 2i\, cn^{-1}\left(\sqrt{\frac{1-k^2x}{x(1-k^2)}},\, k'\right). \quad (24)$$

If $0 > x > -\infty$, the formula (19) offers

$$\int_{x}^{0} \frac{dx}{\sqrt{x(1-x)(1-k^2x)}} = 2i\, sn^{-1}\left(\sqrt{\frac{-x}{1-x}},\, k'\right)$$

$$= 2i\, cn^{-1}\left(\sqrt{\frac{1}{1-x}},\, k'\right); \quad (25)$$

while for the same interval it follows from formula (20) that

$$\int_{-\infty}^{x} \frac{dx}{\sqrt{x(1-x)(1-k^2x)}} = 2i\, sn^{-1}\left(\sqrt{\frac{1}{1-k^2x}},\, k'\right)$$

$$= 2i\, cn^{-1}\left(\sqrt{\frac{-k^2x}{1-k^2x}},\, k'\right). \quad (26)$$

**Art. 28.** Next let $X = (x-\alpha)(x-\beta)(x-\gamma)(x-\delta)$ and further put

$$N = \frac{\sqrt{(\alpha-\gamma)(\beta-\delta)}}{2}, \quad k_3^2 = \frac{(\beta-\gamma)(\alpha-\delta)}{(\alpha-\gamma)(\beta-\delta)}, \quad k_4^2 = \frac{(\alpha-\beta)(\gamma-\delta)}{(\alpha-\gamma)(\beta-\delta)},$$

and note that $k_3^2 + k_4^2 = 1$.

If then $\infty > x > \alpha$, there results, supposing always that $\alpha > \beta > \gamma > \delta$,

$$N \int_\alpha^x \frac{dx}{\sqrt{X}} = sn^{-1}\left[\sqrt{\frac{(\beta-\delta)(x-\alpha)}{(\alpha-\delta)(x-\beta)}}, \; k_3\right]$$

$$= cn^{-1}\left[\sqrt{\frac{(\alpha-\beta)(x-\delta)}{(\alpha-\delta)(x-\beta)}}, \; k_3\right]; \quad . \quad (27)$$

and if $\alpha > x > \beta$

$$N \int_x^\alpha \frac{dx}{\sqrt{-X}} = sn^{-1}\left[\sqrt{\frac{(\beta-\delta)(\alpha-x)}{(\alpha-\beta)(x-\delta)}}, \; k_4\right]$$

$$= cn^{-1}\left[\sqrt{\frac{(\alpha-\delta)(x-\beta)}{(\alpha-\beta)(x-\delta)}}, \; k_4\right]. \quad . \quad (28)$$

If $\alpha > x > \beta$,

$$N \int_\beta^x \frac{dx}{\sqrt{-X}} = sn^{-1}\left[\sqrt{\frac{(\alpha-\gamma)(x-\beta)}{(\alpha-\beta)(x-\gamma)}}, \; k_4\right]$$

$$= cn^{-1}\left[\sqrt{\frac{(\beta-\gamma)(\alpha-x)}{(\alpha-\beta)(x-\gamma)}}, \; k_4\right]; \quad . \quad (29)$$

while if $\beta > x > \gamma$,

$$N \int_x^\beta \frac{dx}{\sqrt{X}} = sn^{-1}\left[\sqrt{\frac{(\alpha-\gamma)(\beta-x)}{(\beta-\gamma)(\alpha-x)}}, \; k_3\right]$$

$$= cn^{-1}\left[\sqrt{\frac{(\alpha-\beta)(x-\gamma)}{(\beta-\gamma)(\alpha-x)}}, \; k_3\right]. \quad . \quad (30)$$

When $x$ lies within the interval $\beta > x > \gamma$,

$$N \int_\gamma^x \frac{dx}{\sqrt{X}} = sn^{-1}\left(\sqrt{\frac{(\beta-\delta)(x-\gamma)}{(\beta-\gamma)(x-\delta)}}, \; k_3\right)$$

$$= cn^{-1}\left(\sqrt{\frac{(\gamma-\delta)(\beta-x)}{(\beta-\gamma)(x-\delta)}}, \; k_3\right); \quad . \quad (31)$$

and when $\gamma > x > \delta$, it is seen that

$$N \int_x^\gamma \frac{dx}{\sqrt{(\alpha-x)(\beta-x)(\gamma-x)(x-\delta)}} = sn^{-1}\left(\sqrt{\frac{(\beta-\delta)(\gamma-x)}{(\gamma-\delta)(\beta-x)}}, \; k_4\right)$$

$$= cn^{-1}\left(\sqrt{\frac{(\beta-\gamma)(x-\delta)}{(\gamma-\delta)(\beta-x)}}, \; k_4\right). \quad . \quad (32)$$

If $\gamma > x > \delta$,

$$N \int_\delta^x \frac{dx}{\sqrt{-X}} = sn^{-1}\left(\sqrt{\frac{(\alpha-\gamma)(x-\delta)}{(\gamma-\delta)(\alpha-x)}}, \; k_4\right)$$

$$= cn^{-1}\left(\sqrt{\frac{(\alpha-\delta)(\gamma-x)}{(\gamma-\delta)(\alpha-x)}}, \; k_4\right), \quad . \quad (33)$$

and if $\delta > x > -\infty$

$$N \int_0^\delta \frac{dx}{\sqrt{X}} = sn^{-1}\left(\sqrt{\frac{(\alpha-\gamma)(\delta-x)}{(\alpha-\delta)(\gamma-x)}}, \; k_3\right)$$

$$= cn^{-1}\left(\sqrt{\frac{(\gamma-\delta)(\alpha-x)}{(\alpha-\delta)(\gamma-x)}}, \; k_3\right). \quad . \quad (34)$$

**Art. 29.** By means of the above formulas it is possible to integrate the reciprocal of the square root of any cubic or biquadratic which has real roots; for example (see Byerly, *Integral Calculus*, 1902, p. 276),

$$\int_0^{\frac{a}{2}} \frac{dx}{\sqrt{(2ax-x^2)(a^2-x^2)}} = \int_x^a \frac{dx}{\sqrt{(2a-x)(a-x)x(a+x)}}$$

$$- \int_{\frac{a}{2}}^a \frac{dx}{\sqrt{(2a-x)(a-x)x(a+x)}} = \frac{1}{a}\left[ sn^{-1}\left(1, \frac{\sqrt{3}}{2}\right)\right.$$

$$\left. - sn^{-1}\left(\frac{\sqrt{6}}{3}, \frac{\sqrt{3}}{2}\right)\right] \quad [\text{cf. (30)}]$$

$$= \frac{1}{a} F\left(\frac{\sqrt{3}}{2}, \sin^{-1} 1\right) - \frac{1}{a} F\left(\frac{\sqrt{3}}{2}, \sin^{-1} \frac{\sqrt{6}}{3}\right).$$

Remark.—In the above integrals it is well to note that (34), for example, may be written

$$N \int_x^\delta \frac{dx}{\sqrt{(\alpha-x)(\beta-x)(\gamma-x)(\delta-x)}},$$

showing that each factor under the root sign is positive for the interval in question.

**Art. 30.** It is seen that the substitution

$$\frac{\alpha-\gamma}{x-\gamma}=\frac{y-\gamma}{\beta-\gamma}, \quad \text{or} \quad \frac{x-\alpha}{x-\gamma}=\frac{\beta-y}{\beta-\gamma} \quad \text{or} \quad \frac{x-\beta}{x-\gamma}=\frac{\alpha-y}{\alpha-\gamma}$$

changes

$$\int_x^\infty \frac{dx}{\sqrt{(x-\alpha)(x-\beta)(x-\gamma)}} \quad \text{into} \quad \int_\gamma^y \frac{dy}{\sqrt{(y-\alpha)(y-\beta)(y-\gamma)}},$$

or (13) into (16). For example,

$$\int_\alpha^\infty \frac{dx}{\sqrt{(x-\alpha)(x-\beta)(x-\gamma)}} = \int_\gamma^\beta \frac{dy}{\sqrt{(y-\alpha)(y-\beta)(y-\gamma)}}$$

$$=\frac{2K}{\sqrt{\alpha-\gamma}}, \quad \cdot \quad (35)$$

where $k^2=\dfrac{\beta-\gamma}{\alpha-\gamma}$, see (16).

By the same substitution (14) becomes (15).
Similarly the substitution

$$\frac{\alpha-x}{\alpha-\beta}=\frac{\alpha-\gamma}{\alpha-y}, \quad \text{or} \quad \frac{x-\beta}{\alpha-\beta}=\frac{\gamma-y}{\alpha-y}, \quad \text{or} \quad \frac{x-\gamma}{\alpha-\gamma}=\frac{\beta-y}{\alpha-y}$$

changes (17) into (20) and shows that

$$\int_\beta^\alpha \frac{dx}{\sqrt{(\alpha-x)(x-\beta)(x-\gamma)}} = \int_{-\infty}^\gamma \frac{dy}{\sqrt{(\alpha-y)(\beta-y)(\gamma-y)}}$$

$$=\frac{2K'}{\sqrt{\alpha-\gamma}} \quad \cdot \quad (36)$$

where $\dfrac{\alpha-\beta}{\alpha-\gamma}=k^2$.

By the same substitution (18) becomes (19).

**Art. 31.** Let the roots of the cubic be one real and two imaginary, so that $X$ has the form $(x-\alpha)[(x-\rho)^2+\sigma^2]$.

Make the substitution

$$y = \frac{X}{(x-\alpha)^2} = \frac{(x-\rho)^2+\sigma^2}{x-\alpha}, \quad \text{or}$$

(1) $(x-\rho)^2+\sigma^2-y(x-\alpha) = 0$, which is an hyperbola.

The condition that this quadratic in $x$ have equal roots, is

(2) $y^2+4(\rho-\alpha)y-4\sigma^2 = 0$.

The roots of this equation are, say,

$$(y_1, y_2) = -2(\rho-\alpha)\pm 2\sqrt{(\rho-\alpha)^2+\sigma^2}.$$

It is evident that $y_1$ is positive and $y_2$ is negative.

If we eliminate $y$ from (1) and (2), we have the biquadratic

$$[(x-\rho)^2+\sigma^2]^2+4(\rho-\alpha)(x-\alpha)[(x-\rho)^2+\sigma^2]-4\sigma^2(x-\alpha)^2 = 0,$$

the left hand side being, as we know *à priori*, a perfect square.

Equating to zero one of these double factors, we have

(3) $\qquad\qquad x^2-2\alpha x+2\alpha\rho-\rho^2-\sigma^2 = 0$.

Further let $x_1$, $x_2$ denote the values of $x$ which correspond to the values $y_1$, $y_2$ of $y$.

From (3) it follows that

$$(x_1, x_2) = \alpha \pm \sqrt{(\alpha-\rho)^2+\sigma^2},$$

or

$$x_1 = \rho+\tfrac{1}{2}y_1, \qquad x_2 = \rho+\tfrac{1}{2}y_2.$$

Further there results

$$y-y_1 = \frac{(x-x_1)^2}{x-\alpha}, \quad y-y_2 = \frac{(x-x_2)^2}{x-\alpha},$$

and

$$\frac{dy}{dx} = \frac{(x-x_1)(x-x_2)}{(x-\alpha)^2}.$$

It follows at once that

$$\int_x^\infty \frac{dx}{\sqrt{X}} = \int_x^\infty \frac{dx}{(x-\alpha)\sqrt{y}} = \int_x^\infty \frac{(x-\alpha)dy}{(x-x_1)(x-x_2)\sqrt{y}}$$

$$= \int_y^\infty \frac{dy}{\sqrt{y(y-y_1)(y-y_2)}} = \frac{2}{\sqrt{y_1-y_2}} cn^{-1}\left(\sqrt{\frac{y-y_1}{y-y_2}}, \sqrt{\frac{-y_2}{y_1-y_2}}\right)$$

$$(\text{cf. } (13)) = \frac{\sqrt{2}}{\sqrt{x_1-x_2}} cn^{-1}\left(\frac{x-x_1}{x-x_2}, k\right), \quad . \quad . \quad (37)$$

where $k^2 = \dfrac{-y_2}{y_1-y_2}$   and   $k'^2 = \dfrac{y_1}{y_1-y_2}$.

In the same way, with the same substitutions, it may be proved that

$$\int_{-\infty}^x \frac{dx}{\sqrt{(\alpha-x)[(x-\rho)^2+\sigma^2]}} = \int_{-\infty}^y \frac{dy}{\sqrt{-y(y_1-y)(y_2-y)}}$$

$$= \frac{2}{\sqrt{y_1-y_2}} cn^{-1}\left(\sqrt{\frac{y_2-y}{y_1-y}}, k'\right)$$

[cf. (20), where $k'^2 = \dfrac{y_1}{y_1-y_2}$ is the complementary modulus of the preceding integral], or

$$\int_{-\infty}^x \frac{dx}{\sqrt{-X}} = \frac{\sqrt{2}}{\sqrt{x_1-x_2}} cn^{-1}\left(\frac{x_2-x}{x_1-x}, k'\right). \quad . \quad . \quad (38)$$

Further write $M^2 = (\rho-\alpha)^2+\sigma^2$, so that $x_1 = \alpha+M$ and $x_2 = \alpha-M$. It is evident that

$$\int_\alpha^x \frac{dx}{\sqrt{(x-\alpha)[(x-\rho)^2+\sigma^2]}} = \int_\infty^y \frac{dy}{\sqrt{y(y-y_1)(y-y_2)}}$$

$$= \frac{\sqrt{2}}{\sqrt{x_1-x_2}} cn^{-1}\left(\frac{x_1-x}{x-x_2}, k\right), \text{ cf. } (37),$$

$$= \frac{1}{\sqrt{M}} cn^{-1}\left[\frac{M-(x-\alpha)}{M+(x-\alpha)}, k\right], k^2 = \frac{1}{2} - \frac{1}{2}\frac{\alpha-\rho}{M}. \quad . \quad (39)$$

Similarly, it may be shown that

$$\int_x^\alpha \frac{dx}{\sqrt{(\alpha-x)[(x-\rho)^2+\sigma^2]}} = \frac{1}{\sqrt{M}} cn^{-1}\left(\frac{M-(\alpha-x)}{M+(\alpha-x)}, k'\right), \quad (40)$$

where

$$k'^2 = \frac{1}{2} + \frac{1}{2}\frac{\alpha-\rho}{M}.$$

Note that the modulus here is the complementary modulus of the one in (39) and that the product of the two moduli is, say,

$$2kk' = \frac{\sigma}{M}.$$

As numerical examples, prove that

$$\int_x^\infty \frac{dx}{\sqrt{x^3-1}} = \frac{1}{\sqrt[4]{3}} cn^{-1}\left(\frac{x-1-\sqrt{3}}{x-1+\sqrt{3}}, k_1\right),$$

$$\int_1^x \frac{dx}{\sqrt{x^3-1}} = \frac{1}{\sqrt[4]{3}} cn^{-1}\left(\frac{\sqrt{3}+1-x}{\sqrt{3}-1+x}, k_1\right),$$

$$\int_x^1 \frac{dx}{\sqrt{1-x^3}} = \frac{1}{\sqrt[4]{3}} cn^{-1}\left(\frac{\sqrt{3}-1+x}{\sqrt{3}+1-x}, k_2\right),$$

$$\int_{-\infty}^x \frac{dx}{\sqrt{1-x^3}} = \frac{1}{\sqrt[4]{3}} cn^{-1}\left(\frac{1-x-\sqrt{3}}{1-x+\sqrt{3}}, k_2\right),$$

where $2k_1k_2 = \frac{1}{2} = \sin 30°$, $k_1 = \sin 15°$, $k_2 = \sin 75°$.

(Greenhill, loc. cit., p. 40.)

**Art. 32.** Suppose next that we have a quartic with two imaginary roots. It is always possible to write

$$X = (ax^2+2bx+c)(Ax^2+2Bx+C),$$

where the real roots constitute the first factor, and the imaginary roots the second so that $b^2-ac$ is positive and $B^2-AC$ is negative.

Make the substitution

$$y = \frac{ax^2+2bx+c}{Ax^2+2Bx+C} = \frac{N}{D}, \text{ say, } \quad . \quad . \quad . \quad . \quad . \quad (i)$$

or

(a) $\qquad\qquad x^2(Ay-a)+2x(By-b)+Cy-c=0.$

This equation has equal roots in $x$, if

(b) $\qquad\qquad (By-b)^2-(Ay-a)(Cy-c)=0.$

Let the roots of this equation be $y_1$ and $y_2$.
From (a) it is seen that

$$[2x(By-b)]^2=x^4(Ay-a)^2+2x^2(Ay-a)(Cy-c)+(Cy-c)^2,$$

which combined with (b), gives

(c) $\qquad -x=\dfrac{Cy-c}{By-b}=\dfrac{By-b}{Ay-a}, \quad Ax+B=\dfrac{Ab-aB}{Ay-a},$

(d) $\qquad y=\dfrac{ax+b}{Ax+B}=\dfrac{bx+c}{Bx+C}, \quad Ay-a=\dfrac{(Ab-aB)x+Ac-aC}{Bx+C}.$

From (i) it follows, if $D$ is put for $Ax^2+2Bx+C$, and since

$Ax_1^2+2Bx_1+C\equiv x_1(Ax_1+B)+Bx_1+C$, that

$$y_1-y=\frac{x-x_1}{D}\,\frac{2(Ab-Ba)xx_1+(Ac-aC)(x+x_1)+2(Bc-bC)}{x_1(Ax_1+B)+(Bx_1+C)},$$

which, see (c) and (d),

$$=\frac{x-x_1}{D}A(y_1-a)\frac{x\{2(Ab-aB)x_1+Ac-aC\}+x_1(Ac-aC)+2(Bc-bC)}{x_1(Ab-aB)+x_1(Ab-aB)+Ac-aC},$$

so that

$$y_1-y=\frac{x-x_1}{D}(Ay_1-a)(x-x_1);$$

and similarly

$$y-y_2=\frac{(a-Ay_2)(x-x_2)^2}{D}$$

and

$$\frac{dy}{dx}=\frac{2(Ab-aB)(x_1-x)(x-x_2)}{D^2}.$$

It follows that

$$\frac{dx}{\sqrt{(ax^2+2bx+c)(Ax^2+2Bx+C)}}$$

$$=\frac{dy}{D\sqrt{y}}=\frac{Ddy}{2(Ab-Ba)(x_1-x)(x-x_2)\sqrt{y}}$$

$$=\frac{\sqrt{(Ay_1-a)(a-Ay_2)}}{2(Ab-aB)}\frac{dy}{\sqrt{y(y_1-y)(y-y_2)}}.$$

Noting that

$$(Ay_1-a)(a-Ay_2)=-A^2y_1y_2+Aa(y_1+y_2)-a^2=\frac{(Ab-aB)^2}{AC-B^2},$$

it follows that

$$(e) \qquad \frac{dx}{\sqrt{X}}=\frac{1}{\sqrt{AC-B^2}}\frac{dy}{\sqrt{4y(y_1-y)(y-y_2)}}.$$

From $(b)$ it is seen that $y_1>0$ and $y_2<0$, and from $(e)$ it is evident that $y$ varies from $0$ to $y_1$ for real values of $\sqrt{X}$. Hence, see $(17)$,

$$\int_x^{x_1}\frac{dx}{\sqrt{X}}=\frac{1}{2\sqrt{AC-B^2}}\int_y^{y_1}\frac{dy}{\sqrt{y(y_1-y)(y-y_2)}},$$

or,

$$\sqrt{y_1-y_2}\sqrt{AC-B^2}\int_x^{x_1}\frac{dx}{\sqrt{X}}=sn^{-1}\left(\sqrt{\frac{y_1-y}{y_1}},k\right)=cn^{-1}\left(\sqrt{\frac{y}{y_1}},k\right)$$

$$(41)$$

where $k^2=\dfrac{y_1}{y_1-y_2}$ and $k'^2=\dfrac{-y_2}{y_1-y_2}$.

**Art. 33.** Suppose next in the quartic

$$X=(ax^2+2bx+c)(Ax^2+2Bx+C),$$

that all the roots are imaginary so that $b^2-ac<0$ and $B^2-AC<0$. In this case the roots $y_1$ and $y_2$ of the equation of the preceding article

$$(AC-B^2)y^2-(Ac+aC-2Bb)y+ac-b^2=0$$

are both positive.

Hence the integral of the equation $(e)$ may be written [cf. (17)] in the form

$$\sqrt{AC-B^2}\int_x^{x_1}\frac{dx}{\sqrt{X}}=\frac{1}{2}\int_y^{y_1}\frac{dy}{\sqrt{-y(y-y_1)(y-y_2)}}$$

$$=\frac{1}{\sqrt{y_1}}sn^{-1}\left(\sqrt{\frac{y_1-y}{y_1-y_2}},\ k\right)=\frac{1}{\sqrt{y_1}}cn^{-1}\left(\sqrt{\frac{y-y_2}{y_1-y_2}},\ k\right)$$

$$=\frac{1}{\sqrt{y_1}}dn^{-1}\left(\sqrt{\frac{y}{y_1}},\ k\right)\ .\ .\ .\ .\ .\ .\ .\ .\ .\ (42)$$

where

$$k^2=1-\frac{y_2}{y_1},\ k'^2=\frac{y_2}{y_1}$$

and where $y$ oscillates between the two positive values $y_1$ and $y_2$.

**Art. 34.** As an example of the preceding article, let

$$X=x^4+2v^2x^2\cos 2\omega+v^4=(x^2+2vx\sin\omega+v^2)(x^2-2vx\sin\omega+v^2).$$

If we put

$$y=\frac{x^2+2vx\sin\omega+v^2}{x^2-2vx\sin\omega+v^2},$$

it is seen that

$$y_1=\tan^2\left(\frac{\pi}{4}+\frac{\omega}{2}\right),\ y_2=\tan^2\left(\frac{\pi}{4}-\frac{\omega}{2}\right),\ x_1=v,\ x_2=-v,$$

$$k=\frac{1-\sin\omega}{1+\sin\omega}=\tan^2\left(\frac{\pi}{4}-\frac{\omega}{2}\right),$$

and

$$\int_x^v\frac{dx}{\sqrt{x^4+2v^2x^2\cos 2\omega+v^4}}$$

$$=\frac{1}{v(1+\sin\omega)}dn^{-1}\sqrt{\frac{1-\sin\omega}{1+\sin\omega}\cdot\frac{x^2+2vx\sin\omega+v^2}{x^2-2vx\sin\omega+v^2}}.\quad(43)$$

When $\omega=\frac{\pi}{4}$, $v=1$, the preceding equation becomes

$$\int_x^1\frac{dx}{\sqrt{1+x^4}}=(2-\sqrt{2})dn^{-1}\left\{(\sqrt{2}-1)\sqrt{\frac{x^2+\sqrt{2}x+1}{x^2-\sqrt{2}x+1}},\ k\right\}\ .\quad(44)$$

where $\quad k=(\sqrt{2}-1)^2.$

For the substitution $\dfrac{x^2}{v^2} = \dfrac{1+z}{1-z}$, there results

$$\int_x^\infty \frac{dx}{\sqrt{x^4 + 2v^2x^2 \cos 2\omega + v^4}} = \frac{1}{2v}\int_z^1 \frac{dz}{\sqrt{(1-z^2)(\cos^2 \omega + z^2 \sin^2 \omega)}},$$

which, see (2),

$$= \frac{1}{2v} cn^{-1}(z, \sin \omega) = \frac{1}{2v} cn^{-1}\left(\frac{x^2 - v^2}{x^2 + v^2}, \sin \omega\right).$$

If in this formula we put $\omega = \frac{1}{4}\pi$ and $v = 1$, we have

$$\int_x^\infty \frac{dx}{\sqrt{x^4 + 1}} = \frac{1}{2} cn^{-1}\left(\frac{x^2 - 1}{x^2 + 1}, \frac{1}{2}\sqrt{2}\right),$$

$$\int_0^x \frac{dx}{\sqrt{1 + x^4}} = \frac{1}{2} cn^{-1}\left(\frac{1 - x^2}{1 + x^2}, \frac{1}{2}\sqrt{2}\right).$$

**Art. 35.** It was shown above that the substitution

$$\sin^2 \phi = \frac{1 - x^2}{1 - k^2x^2}$$

transforms the integral

$(A)$ $\qquad \displaystyle\int_x^1 \frac{dx}{\sqrt{(1-x^2)(1-k^2x^2)}}$ into $sn^{-1}\left(\sqrt{\dfrac{1-x^2}{1-k^2x^2}}, k\right)$.

On the other hand

$(B)$ $\qquad \displaystyle\int_x^1 \frac{dx}{\sqrt{(1-x^2)(1-k^2x^2)}} = \int_0^1 \frac{dx}{\sqrt{(1-x^2)(1-k^2x^2)}}$

$$- \int_0^x \frac{dx}{\sqrt{(1-x^2)(1-k^2x^2)}} = K - u,$$

where

$$u = \int_0^x \frac{dx}{\sqrt{(1-x^2)(1-k^2x^2)}}.$$

It follows that

$$sn^{-1}\sqrt{\frac{1-x^2}{1-k^2x^2}} = K - sn^{-1}x,$$

a relation among the integrals. It is also at once evident that

$$\sqrt{\frac{1-x^2}{1-k^2x^2}} = sn(K-u), \quad \text{or} \quad \frac{cn\,u}{dn\,u} = sn(K-u),$$

which is a relation among the functions.

In $(A)$ make $k=0$, and then

$$\int_0^1 \frac{dx}{\sqrt{1-x^2}} = \sin^{-1}\sqrt{1-x^2},$$

and from $(B)$ it is seen that

$$\int_x^1 \frac{dx}{\sqrt{1-x^2}} = \int_0^1 \frac{dx}{\sqrt{1-x^2}} - \int_0^x \frac{dx}{\sqrt{1-x^2}} = \frac{\pi}{2} - u,$$

if

$$u = \int_0^x \frac{dx}{\sqrt{1-x^2}} = \sin^{-1} x.$$

Hence

$$\sin^{-1}\sqrt{1-x^2} = \frac{\pi}{2} - \sin^{-1} x.$$

a relation among the integrals; and on the other hand it is seen that

$$\sqrt{1-\sin^2 u} = \sin\left(\frac{\pi}{2} - u\right),$$

a relation among the functions.

It is thus made evident that we may study the nature of the elliptic functions and their characteristic properties directly from their associated integrals just as we may study the properties of the circular, hyperbolic, logarithmic and exponential functions from their associated integrals. This should be emphasized both in the study of the elementary calculus and in the theory of elliptic integrals and elliptic functions.

**Art. 36.** In the applications of the elementary calculus it was often necessary to evaluate such integrals as $\int \sin u\, du$; so here we must study the integrals of the most usual elliptic functions. From the integral $u = \int_0^\phi \frac{d\phi}{\Delta\phi}$, it is seen at once that

$du = \dfrac{d\phi}{\Delta\phi}$, or $dn\,u\,du = d\phi$, so that $d\,am\,u = dn\,u\,du$, $d\,sn\,u = cn\,u\,dn\,u\,du$, $d\,cn\,u = -sn\,u\,dn\,u\,du$, $d\,dn\,u = -k^2cn\,u\,sn\,u\,du$. We further note that

$$sn^2u + cn^2u = 1,\ dn^2u - k'^2 = k^2cn^2u,\ dn^2u + k^2sn^2u = 1.$$

We have without difficulty

$$\int sn\,u\,du = -\frac{1}{k^2}\int \frac{-k^2sn\,u\,cn\,u\,du}{cn\,u} = -\frac{1}{k}\int \frac{dv}{\sqrt{v^2 - k'^2}},$$

(if $v = dn\,u$). The last integral is

$$-\frac{1}{k}\log\left(v + \sqrt{v^2 - k'^2}\right) = -\frac{1}{k}\cosh^{-1}\frac{v}{k'} = -\frac{1}{k}\cosh^{-1}\left(\frac{dn\,u}{k'}\right).$$

Further since $dn\,K = k'$, Art. 17, we have

$$k\int_u^K sn\,u\,du = \cosh^{-1}\left(\frac{dn\,u}{k'}\right) = \sinh^{-1}\left(k\frac{cn\,u}{k'}\right) = \log\frac{dn\,u + kcn\,u}{k'}.$$

Similarly it may be proved that

$$k\int_0^u cn\,u\,du = \cos^{-1}(dn\,u) = \sin^{-1}(ksn\,u),$$

and

$$\int_0^u dn\,u\,du = \phi = am\,u = \sin^{-1}sn\,u = \cos^{-1}cn\,u.$$

**Art. 37.** The following integrals should be noted:

$$\int \frac{du}{sn\,u} = \int \frac{sn\,u\,cn\,u\,dn\,u\,du}{sn^2u\,cn\,u\,dn\,u} = \frac{1}{2}\int \frac{dv}{v\sqrt{(1-v)(1-k^2v)}}\ \text{(if } v = sn^2u).$$

Further writing $\sqrt{(1-v)(1-k^2v)} = (1-v)z$, the last integral becomes

$$-\frac{1}{2}\log\left[\frac{\sqrt{(1-v)(1-k^2v)} + 1}{v} - \frac{1+k^2}{2}\right] - \frac{1}{2}\log\frac{1-k^2}{2}$$

$$= -\frac{1}{2}\log\left[\frac{cn\,u\,dn\,u + 1}{sn^2u} - \frac{1+k^2}{2}\right] + C$$

$$= -\frac{1}{2}\log\left[\frac{2cn\,u\,dn\,u + cn^2u + dn^2u}{2sn^2u}\right] + C,$$

so that, omitting $C$,

$$\int \frac{du}{sn\,u} = \log\left[\frac{sn\,u}{cn\,u + dn\,u}\right],$$

where the arbitrary constant is omitted.   Similarly it may be shown that

$$\int \frac{du}{cn\,u} = \frac{1}{k'} \log \left[ \frac{k'sn\,u + dn\,u}{cn\,u} \right],$$

and that

$$\int \frac{du}{dn\,u} = \frac{1}{2k'} \sin^{-1} \left[ \frac{k'^2sn^2u - cn^2u}{dn^2u} \right].$$

Further by definition $E(k, \phi) = \int_0^\phi \Delta\phi\,d\phi$ (cf. Art. 5), or since $\phi = am\,u$ and $d\,am\,u = dn\,u\,du$,

$$E(am\,u) = \int_0^u dn^2u\,du.$$

It follows that

$$\int_0^u sn^2u\,du = \frac{1}{k^2}[u - E(am\,u, k)],$$

and

$$\int_0^u cn^2u\,du = \frac{1}{k^2}[E(am\,u, k) - k'^2u].$$

**Art. 38.** *Reduction formulas.*   The following is a very useful and a very general reduction formula.*   Consider the identity

$$(m+\sin^2\phi)^\mu \sin\phi\cos\phi\Delta\phi = \int_0^\phi \frac{d}{d\phi}\{(m+\sin^2\phi)^\mu \sin\phi\cos\phi\Delta\phi\}d\phi$$

$$= \int_0^\phi \{2\mu(m+\sin^2\phi)^{\mu-1}\sin^2\phi\cos^2\phi\Delta^2\phi$$

$$+ (m+\sin^2\phi)^\mu[\cos^2\phi\Delta^2\phi - \sin^2\phi\Delta^2\phi - k^2\sin^2\phi\cos^2\phi]\} \frac{d\phi}{\Delta\phi}.$$

In this expression put $m+\sin^2\phi = v$, so that $\sin^2\phi = v-m$, $\cos^2\phi = 1-v+m$, $\Delta^2\phi = 1-k^2v+k^2m$, and writing

$$V_\mu = \int_0^\phi \frac{v^\mu d\phi}{\Delta\phi} = \int_0^\phi \frac{(m+\sin^2\phi)^\mu d\phi}{\Delta\phi},$$

---

* See, for example, Durège, *Elliptische Funktionen*, § 4, Second edition.

then there is found

$$(m+\sin^2\phi)^\mu \sin\phi \cos\phi\,\Delta\phi = -2\mu A V_{\mu-1} + (2\mu+1)BV_\mu$$
$$-(2\mu+2)CV_{\mu+1} + (2\mu+3)k^2 V_{\mu+2}, \quad . \quad . \quad (i)$$

where $A = m(1+m)(1+k^2m)$;

$\quad B = 1+2m+2k^2m+3k^2m^2$;

$\quad C = 1+k^2+3k^2m$.

From this formula it is evident that every integral $V_\mu$ may be expressed through the three integrals $V_0$, $V_1$, $V_{-1}$, the latter being forms of integrals which in Chapter I have been called *elliptic integrals of the first, second and third kinds* respectively.

The following formulas may be derived immediately from the formula above, by writing

$$S_m(u) = \int sn^m u\,du, \quad C_m(u) = \int cn^m u\,du, \quad D_m(u) = \int dn^m u\,du,$$

$$(n+1)k^2 S_{n+2}(u) - n(1+k^2)S_n(u) + (n-1)S_{n-2}(u)$$
$$= sn^{-1}u\,cn\,u\,dn\,u, \quad . \quad (ii)$$

$$(n+1)k^2 C_{n+2}(u) + n(k'^2-k^2)C_n(u) - (n-1)k'^2 C_{n-2}(u)$$
$$= cn^{-1}u\,sn\,u\,dn\,u, \quad . \quad (iii)$$

$$(n+1)D_{n+2}(u) - n(1+k'^2)D_n(u) + (n-1)k'^2 D_{n-2}(u)$$
$$= k^2 dn^{-1}u\,sn\,u\,cn\,u. \quad . \quad (iv)$$

In particular, if $u = K$ say in $(ii)$, there results

$$(n+1)k^2 S_{n+2}(K) - n(1+k^2)S_n(K) + (n-1)S_{n-2}(K) = 0,$$

which is the analogue of Wallis's formula for $\int_0^{\frac{\pi}{2}} \sin^n \theta\,d\theta$.

**Art. 39.** It may be noted that any of the quantities $F(\sin^2\phi)$, $F(\cos^2\phi)$, $F(\tan^2\phi)$, where $F$ is a rational function of its argument, may be expressed through an aggregate of terms of the form $M(m+\sin^2\phi)^\mu$, where $\mu$ is a positive or negative integer or zero and where $M$ and $m$ are real or imaginary constants.

Further by writing $x = \dfrac{a+bz}{c+dz}$, where $z = \sin\phi$, or $z = \cos\phi$, or $z = \tan \phi$, it is seen that the general elliptic integral of Art. 5, namely, $\int \frac{Q(x)dx}{\sqrt{R(x)}}$ may be put in the form $\int \frac{F(\sin^2 \phi)d\phi}{\Delta \phi}$, which in turn may be expressed through integrals that correspond to the integrals $V_0$, $V_1$ and $V_{-1}$ of the preceding article.

**Art. 40.** Returning to formula $(i)$ above, make $\mu = -1$, and note that if $m = 0$, we have $A = 0$, $B = 1$; the formula becomes

$(a)$ $\qquad \cot \phi \, \Delta \phi = -\int \frac{1}{\sin^2 \phi} \frac{d\phi}{\Delta \phi} + k^2 \int \frac{\sin^2 \phi \, d\phi}{\Delta \phi}$.

Next let $m = -1$, so that $A = 0$, $B = -k'^2$, and we have

$(b)$ $\qquad -\tan \phi \, \Delta \phi = -k'^2 \int \frac{1}{\cos^2 \phi} \frac{d\phi}{\Delta \phi} - k^2 \int \frac{\cos^2 \phi \, d\phi}{\Delta \phi}$;

finally let $m = -\frac{1}{k^2}$, so that $A = 0$, $B = \frac{k'^2}{k^2}$, and the reduction formula is

$(c)$ $\qquad -\frac{k^2 \sin \phi \cos \phi}{\Delta \phi} = k'^2 \int \frac{1}{\Delta^2 \phi} \frac{d\phi}{\Delta \phi} - \int \Delta \phi \, d\phi$.

**Art. 41.** Legendre, *Traité, etc.*, I, p. 256, offers the following integrals " which are often met with in the application of the elliptic integrals." These may for the most part be derived at once from the formulas given above.

$\int_0^\phi \frac{d\phi}{\Delta \phi} = F(k, \phi)$, where $\Delta \phi = \sqrt{1 - k^2 \sin^2 \phi} = \Delta$,

$\int_0^\phi \Delta \, d\phi = E(k, \phi)$, or $\int_0^u dn^2 u \, du = E(u)$, since $d\phi = dn \, u \, du$.

$\int_0^\phi \frac{d\phi}{\Delta^3} = \frac{1}{k'^2} E(k, \phi) - \frac{k^2 \sin \phi \cos \phi}{k'^2 \Delta}$, or

$\int_0^u \frac{du}{dn^2 u} = \frac{E(u)}{k'^2} - \frac{k^2 sn \, u \, cn \, u}{k'^2 dn \, u}$,

$\int_0^\phi \frac{d\phi \sin^2 \phi}{\Delta} = \frac{1}{k^2}[F(k, \phi) - E(k, \phi)]$, or

$$\int_0^u sn^2 u\, du = \frac{u - E(u)}{k^2},$$

$$\int_0^\phi \frac{d\phi \cos^2 \phi}{\Delta} = \frac{1}{k^2}[E(k,\ \phi) - k'^2 F(k,\ \phi)],\ \text{or}$$

$$\int_0^u cn^2 u\, du = \frac{-k'^2 u + E(u)}{k^2}.$$

$$\int_0^\phi \frac{d\phi}{\Delta \cos^2 \phi} = \frac{1}{k'^2}[\Delta \tan \phi + k'^2 F(k,\ \phi) - E(k,\ \phi)],\ \text{or}$$

$$\int_0^u \frac{du}{cn^2 u} = \frac{tn\, u\, dn\, u + k'^2 u - E(u)}{k'^2},$$

$$\int_0^\phi \frac{d\phi \tan^2 \phi}{\Delta} = \frac{\Delta \tan \phi - E(k,\ \phi)}{k'^2},\ \text{or}$$

$$\int_0^u tn^2 u\, du = \frac{dn\, u\, tn\, u - E(u)}{k'^2}.$$

$$\int_0^\phi \frac{d\phi \cos^2 \phi}{\Delta^3} = \frac{1}{k^2}[F(k,\ \phi) - E(k,\ \phi)] + \frac{\sin \phi \cos \phi}{\Delta},$$

$$\int_0^\phi \frac{d\phi \sin^2 \phi}{\Delta^3} = \frac{1}{k^2 k'^2}[E(k,\ \phi) - k'^2 F(k,\ \phi)] - \frac{\sin \phi \cos \phi}{k'^2 \Delta},$$

$$\int_0^\phi \frac{\Delta\, d\phi}{\cos^2 \phi} = \Delta \tan \phi + F(k,\ \phi) - E(k,\ \phi),$$

$$\int_0^\phi \Delta \tan^2 \phi\, d\phi = \Delta \tan \phi + F(k,\ \phi) - 2E(k,\ \phi),$$

$$\int_0^\phi \Delta^3 d\phi = \frac{k^2}{3}\Delta \sin \phi \cos \phi + \frac{2 + 2k'^2}{3}E(k,\ \phi) - \frac{k'^2}{3}F(k,\ \phi),$$

$$\int_0^\phi \Delta \sin^2 \phi\, d\phi = \frac{-1}{3}\Delta \sin \phi \cos \phi + \frac{2k^2 - 1}{3k^2}E(k,\ \phi) + \frac{k'^2}{3k^2}F(k,\ \phi),$$

$$\int_0^\phi \Delta \cos^2 \phi\, d\phi = \frac{1}{3}\Delta \sin \phi \cos \phi + \frac{1 + k^2}{3k^2}E(k,\ \phi) - \frac{k'^2}{3k^2}F(k,\ \phi).$$

To these may be added

$$\int_\phi^{\frac{\pi}{2}} \frac{d\phi}{\sin^2 \phi \Delta} = \cot \phi \Delta \phi + K - E_1 - F(k,\ \phi) + E(k,\ \phi),\ \text{or}$$

$$\int_u^K \frac{du}{sn^2u} = cot\ am\ u\ dn\ u + K - E_1 - u + E(u),$$

$$\int_u^K \frac{du}{tn^2u} = cot\ am\ u\ dn\ u - E_1 + E(u),\ \text{or}$$

$$\int_\phi^{\frac{\pi}{2}} \frac{d\phi}{\tan^2\phi\ \Delta} = \int_\phi^{\frac{\pi}{2}} \frac{1 - \sin^2\phi}{\sin^2\phi} \frac{d\phi}{\Delta\phi}.$$

## EXAMPLES

1. Show that

$$\int_x^1 \frac{dx}{\sqrt{1-x^4}} = \tfrac{1}{2}\sqrt{2}\,cn^{-1}(x, \tfrac{1}{2}\sqrt{2}),$$

$$\int_1^x \frac{dx}{\sqrt{x^4-1}} = \tfrac{1}{2}\sqrt{2}\,cn^{-1}\left(\frac{1}{x}, \tfrac{1}{2}\sqrt{2}\right).$$

2. Show that

$$\int_0^1 \sqrt{1-x^4}\,dx = 2\sqrt{2}\int_0^K (dn^2x - dn^4x)dx = \frac{\sqrt{2}}{3}K\left(\text{mod }\frac{\sqrt{2}}{2}\right) = 0.8740\,1\ldots$$

3. Show that $\int_0^b \sqrt{\dfrac{a^2-bx}{bx-x^2}}\,dx = 2a\int_0^K dn^2x\,dx = 2aE\left(\dfrac{b}{a}, \dfrac{\pi}{2}\right).$

4. Show that $\int_0^K \dfrac{sn\,u\,du}{dn\,u+k'} = \dfrac{1}{k'(1+k')}.$

5. If $u = \int_0^b \sqrt{(a^2-x^2)(b^2-x^2)}\,dx$, write $y = sn^{-1}\left(\dfrac{x}{b}, \dfrac{b}{a}\right)$, cf. formula $(5a)$, and show that

$$u = ab^2\int_0^K cn^2y\ dn^2y\ dy = \tfrac{1}{3}a\left[(a^2+b^2)E\left(\frac{b}{a}, \frac{\pi}{2}\right) - (a^2-b^2)K\right],\ \left(\text{mod. }\frac{b}{a}\right).$$

*Byerly.*

6. Show that for the inverse functions,

$(i)$ $\qquad \int sn^{-1}u\,du = u\,sn^{-1}u + \dfrac{1}{k}\cosh\left(\dfrac{\sqrt{1-k^2u^2}}{k'}\right);$

$(ii)$ $\qquad \int cn^{-1}u\,du = u\,cn^{-1}u - \dfrac{1}{k}\cos^{-1}(\sqrt{k'^2+k^2u^2});$

$(iii)$ $\qquad \int dn^{-1}u\,du = u\,dn^{-1}u - \sin^{-1}\left(\dfrac{\sqrt{1-u^2}}{k}\right).$

7. Note that if $X = ax^2 + 2bx + c$,

$$d[x^p \sqrt{X}] = \frac{a(p+1)x^{p+1} + b(2p+1)x^p + cpx^{p-1}}{\sqrt{X}} dx;$$

or, if we put $v_p = \int \dfrac{x^p dx}{\sqrt{X}}$, we have

$$x^p \sqrt{X} = a(p+1)v_{p+1} + b(2p+1)v_p + cpv_{p-1}.$$

Further, if $t = sn^2 u$, it is seen that

$$\int sn^m u \, du = \tfrac{1}{2} \int \frac{t^{\frac{m-1}{2}} dt}{\sqrt{(1-t)(1-k^2 t)}}.$$

Derive the reduction formulas $(ii)$, $(iii)$, $(iv)$ of Art. 38.

8. Prove that $\displaystyle\int \frac{dS}{\dfrac{x^2}{a^2} + \dfrac{y^2}{b^2} + \dfrac{z^2}{c^2}} = \frac{4\pi abc}{\sqrt{a^2 - c^2}} cn^{-1}\left(\frac{c}{a}, \sqrt{\frac{a^2 - b^2}{a^2 - c^2}}\right),$

where the integration is taken over the surface $S$ of a sphere $x^2 + y^2 + z^2 = r^2$.

*Burnside, Math. Tripos*, 1881

9. Show that

$$\int \frac{sn\, u}{cn\, u} du = \frac{1}{k'} \log \frac{dn\, u + k'}{cn\, u},$$

$$\int \frac{cn\, u}{sn\, u} du = \log \frac{1 - dn\, u}{sn\, u},$$

$$\int \frac{sn\, u}{cn\, u\, dn\, u} du = \frac{1}{k'^2} \log \frac{dn\, u}{cn\, u},$$

$$\int \frac{cn\, u}{sn^2\, u} du = -\frac{dn\, u}{sn\, u},$$

$$\int \frac{sn\, u}{cn^2\, u} du = -\frac{1}{k'^2} \frac{dn\, u}{cn\, u}.$$

# CHAPTER IV

## THE NUMERICAL COMPUTATION OF THE ELLIPTIC INTE-
## GRALS OF THE FIRST AND SECOND KINDS.  LANDEN'S
## TRANSFORMATIONS

**Art. 42.** With Jacobi * consider two fixed circles as in
Fig. 15 and suppose that $R$ is the radius of the larger circle and
$r$ the radius of the smaller circle.  Let the distance $OQ=l$.
From any point $B$ on the large circle draw a tangent to the small

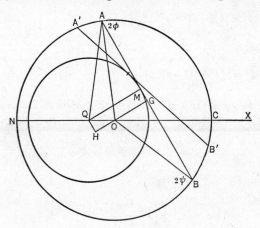

Fig. 15.

circle which again cuts the large circle in $A$.  Denote the azimuth
angle $BOX$ by $2\psi$ and $AOX$ by $2\phi$.  $OG$ is drawn perpendicular
to $AB$ and its length is denoted by $p$.  Note that the angle
$GOX = \phi - \psi$ and $GOB = \phi + \psi$, $p = R \cos(\phi + \psi)$ and $QM = r =$
$p + OH = R \cos(\phi + \psi) + l \cos(\phi - \psi)$, or

$$r = (R+l) \cos \phi \cos \psi - (R-l) \sin \phi \sin \psi.$$

* Jacobi, *Crelle's Journal*, Vol. III, p. 376, 1828; see also Cayley's *Elliptic
Functions*, p. 28.

When $\psi = 0$, let the corresponding value of $\phi$ be $\mu$, so that

$$r = (R+l) \cos \mu, \text{ or } \cos \mu = \frac{r}{R+l}, \sin \mu = \frac{\sqrt{(R+l)^2 - r^2}}{R+l}.$$

Denote the ratio $\frac{QN}{QC}$ by $\Delta\mu$, so that $\Delta\mu = \frac{R-l}{R+l}$; then since

$\Delta\mu^2 = 1 - k^2 \sin^2 \mu$, it is seen that $k^2 = \frac{4lR}{(R+l)^2 - r^2}$.

Returning to the figure, it is seen that

$$\overline{AM}^2 = \overline{AQ}^2 - \overline{MQ}^2 = R^2 + l^2 + 2Rl \cos 2\phi - r^2$$
$$= (R+l)^2 - r^2 - 4lR \sin^2 \phi;$$

or

$$\overline{AM}^2 = \{(R+l)^2 - r^2\}\Delta^2\phi;$$

and similarly

$$\overline{BM}^2 = \{(R+l)^2 - r^2\}\Delta^2 \psi.$$

If the tangent is varied, its new position becoming $A'B'$, consecutive to the initial position, then clearly we have

$$AA' : BB' = AM : BM;$$

or

$$\frac{d\phi}{AM} + \frac{d\psi}{BM} = 0;$$

and if for $AM$ and $BM$ their values be substituted, it follows that

$$\frac{d\phi}{\Delta\phi} + \frac{d\psi}{\Delta\psi} = 0.$$

Suppose that the smaller circle is varied, the centre moving along the $X$-axis while $r$ and $l$ are subjected to the condition

$$k^2 = \frac{4lR}{(R+l)^2 - r^2}, \ k \text{ being constant.}$$

In particular when the smaller circle reduces to the point circle at $L$, as in Fig. 16, then

$$r = 0, \quad OL = l \text{ and } k^2 = \frac{4lR}{(R+l)^2}.$$

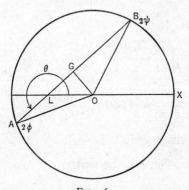

FIG. 16.

Let $\theta$ represent the angle $XLA$. It is seen that

$$\theta = \frac{\pi}{2} + \phi + \psi,$$

and consequently $d\theta = d\phi + d\psi$.

It is also seen that the angle $LAO = \theta - 2\phi$ and $GOX = \phi + \psi$. From the triangle $ALO$ it follows at once that

$$l \sin \theta = R \sin (2\phi - \theta). \quad \ldots \quad (1)$$

The relation $\dfrac{d\phi}{AM} + \dfrac{d\psi}{BM} = 0$, becomes here

$$\frac{d\phi}{AM} = \frac{d\psi}{BM} = \frac{d\theta}{2AG};$$

or, since

$$\overline{AG}^2 = R^2 - l^2 \cos^2 (180 - \phi - \psi) = R^2 - l^2 \sin^2 \theta,$$

it follows that

$$\frac{d\phi}{\Delta\phi} = \frac{d\theta \,(R+l)}{2\sqrt{R^2 - l^2 \sin^2 \theta}}. \quad \ldots \quad (2)$$

Formula (1) may be regarded as the algebraic integral* of (2), or (2) may be considered as being produced by the transformation (1).

Write $k_1 = \dfrac{l}{R}$ and put $\phi_1$ in the place of $\theta$.

It is seen that

$$k = \frac{2\sqrt{lR}}{R+l} = \frac{2\sqrt{k_1}}{1+k_1}, \; k' = \frac{1-k_1}{1+k_1}, \; k_1 = \frac{1-k'}{1+k''}, \quad . \quad . \quad (3)$$

and

$$\frac{d\phi}{\Delta(k,\,\phi)} = \frac{1}{2}(1+k_1)\,\frac{d\phi_1}{\Delta(k_1,\,\phi_1)}, \quad . \quad . \quad . \quad . \quad (2')$$

$$k_1 \sin\phi_1 = \sin(2\phi - \phi_1). \quad . \quad . \quad . \quad . \quad . \quad (1')$$

The last expression may be written

$$k_1 \sin(\phi_1 - \phi + \phi) = \sin(\phi - \phi_1 + \phi),$$

from which we have at once

$$\tan(\phi_1 - \phi) = \frac{1-k_1}{1+k_1}\tan\phi = k'\tan\phi, \quad . \quad . \quad (3)$$

or

$$\tan\phi_1 = \frac{(1+k')\tan\phi}{1-k'\tan^2\phi}, \; \sin\phi_1 = \frac{(1+k')\sin\phi\cos\phi}{\Delta(k,\,\phi)}.$$

**Art. 43.** It is seen that $k_1 = \dfrac{l}{r} < 1$ and since $\dfrac{2\sqrt{k_1}}{1+k_1} > k_1$, it follows that $k > k_1$. From (1') it is seen that $0 < \phi < \phi_1$, if $\phi \leqq \dfrac{\pi}{2}$.

From (2') it is seen that

$$F(k,\,\phi) = \frac{1}{2}(1+k_1)F(k_1,\,\phi_1)$$

$$= (1+k_1)(1+k_2)\;\ldots\;(1+k_n)\frac{F(k_n,\,\phi_n)}{2^n}, \quad . \quad (A)$$

---

* John Landen, An investigation of a general theorem for finding the length of an arc of any conic, etc., Phil. Trans. 65 (1775), pp. 283, et. seq.; or *Mathematical Memoirs* I, p. 32 of John Landen (London, 1780). An article by Cayley on John Landen is given in the Encyc. Brit., Eleventh Edition, Vol. XVI, p. 153. See also Lagrange, *Œuvres*, II, p. 253; Legendre, *Traité*, etc., I, p. 89.

where the moduli are decreasing and the amplitudes are increasing.

It is also seen that

$$k_v = \frac{1 - \sqrt{1 - k^2_{v-1}}}{1 + \sqrt{1 - k^2_{v-1}}}, \quad \left(\begin{matrix} v = 1, 2, \ldots, n \\ k_0 = k \end{matrix}\right),$$

$$\tan(\phi_v - \phi_{v-1}) = \sqrt{1 - k^2_{v-1}} \tan \phi_{v-1}. \quad . \quad (i)$$

It is further evident that $F(k_n, \phi_n)$ approaches the limit $\int_0^\Phi d\phi = \Phi$, where $\Phi$ is the limiting value of $\phi$ as $n$ increases.

If $\phi = \frac{\pi}{2}$, it follows at once from $(i)$, see also Art. 49, that

$$\phi_1 = \pi, \ \phi_2 = 2\pi, \ \ldots, \ \phi_n = 2^{n-1}\pi,$$

and consequently

$$K = F\left(k, \frac{\pi}{2}\right) = \frac{\pi}{2}(1 + k_1)(1 + k_2)(1 + k_3). \ \ldots$$

**Art. 44.** Suppose, for example, that it is required to find $F(\frac{1}{2}, 40°)$. Using the seven-place logarithm tables of Vega, it is found that for

$$\phi = 40, \ \sin \theta = k = \tfrac{1}{2}, \ \text{or} \ \theta = 30,$$

$$\sqrt{1 - k^2} = k' = 0.86603$$

| | |
|---|---|
| $1 - k' = 0.13397$ | $\log(1 - k') = 9.1270076$ |
| $1 + k' = 1.86603$ | $\text{colog}(1 + k') = 9.7290814$ |
| $k_1 = 0.071794$ | $\log k_1 = 8.8560890$ |
| $1 - k_1 = 0.928206$ | $\log(1 - k_1) = 9.9676444$ |
| $1 + k_1 = 1.071794$ | $\log(1 + k_1) = 0.0301098$ |
| | $\log k_1^2 = 9.9977542$ |
| $k'_1 = 0.997418$ | $\log k'_1 = 9.9988771$ |
| $1 - k'_1 = 0.002582$ | $\log(1 - k'_1) = 7.4121244$ |
| $1 + k'_1 = 1.997418$ | $\text{colog}(1 + k'_1) = 9.6995263$ |
| $k_2 = 0.001293$ | $\log k_2 = 7.1116507$ |

$$1 - k_2 = 0.998707 \qquad \log(1 - k_2) = 9.9994381$$
$$1 + k_2 = 1.001293 \qquad \log(1 + k_2) = 0.0005599$$

$$\log k'^2 = 9.9999980$$
$$k'_2 = 1 \qquad\qquad \log k'_2 = 9.9999990$$
$$k_3 = 0$$

$$\log k' = 9.9375329$$
$$\log \tan \phi = 9.9238135$$

$$\log \tan(\phi_1 - \phi) = 9.8613464$$
$$\phi_1 - \phi = 36° \qquad 0' \qquad 20''$$
$$\phi_1 = 76° \qquad 0' \qquad 20''$$

$$\log k'_1 = 9.9988771$$
$$\log \tan \phi_1 = 0.6034084$$

$$\log \tan(\phi_2 - \phi_1) = 0.6022855$$
$$\phi_2 - \phi_1 = 75° \qquad 58' \qquad 15''$$
$$\phi_2 = 151° \qquad 58' \qquad 35''$$

$$\tan(\phi_3 - \phi_2) = \tan \phi_2$$
$$\Phi = \phi_3 = 2\phi_2 = 303° \qquad 57' \qquad 10''$$
$$\frac{1}{2^3}\Phi = 37° \qquad 59' \qquad 39''$$

$$= 136779''$$
$$\pi = 648000''$$
$$\log\left(\frac{1}{2^3}\Phi\right)'' = 5.1360194$$
$$\text{colog } \pi'' = 4.1884250$$
$$\log \pi = 0.4971499$$

$$\log\left(\frac{1}{2^3}\Phi\right) = 9.8215943$$

$$\log(1 + k_1) = 0.0301098$$
$$\log(1 + k_2) = 0.0005599$$
$$\log\left(\frac{1}{2^3}\Phi\right) = 9.8215943$$

$$\log F(\tfrac{1}{2}, 40°) = 9.8522640$$
$$F(\tfrac{1}{2}, 40°) = .711646$$

The value given in Legendre's tables is
$$.7116472757$$

**Art. 45.**  The formulas of Art. 42 may be used to increase the modulus and decrease the amplitude; for if the subscripts be interchanged, it is seen that

$$F(k, \phi) = \frac{2}{1+k} F(k_1, \phi_1), \quad \ldots \ldots \quad (i)$$

$$k_1 = \frac{2\sqrt{k}}{1+k},$$

$$\sin(2\phi_1 - \phi) = k \sin \phi,$$

where $k_1 > k$ and $\phi_1 < \phi$.

Applying the formula $(i)$ $n$ times, there results

$$F(k, \phi) = \frac{2}{1+k} \cdot \frac{2}{1+k_1} \cdot \ldots \cdot \frac{2}{1+k_{n-1}} F(k_n, \phi_n);$$

or, since

$$\frac{2}{1+k} = \frac{k_1}{\sqrt{k}}, \quad \frac{2}{1+k_1} = \frac{k_2}{\sqrt{k_1}}, \text{ etc.},$$

it is seen that

$$F(k, \phi) = k_n \sqrt{\frac{k_1 k_2 \ldots k_{n-1}}{k}} \, F(k_n, \phi_n),$$

where

$$k_v = \frac{2\sqrt{k_{v-1}}}{1+k_{v-1}}, \quad \sin(2\phi_v - \phi_{v-1})$$

$$= k_{v-1} \sin \phi_{v-1} (v = 1, 2, \ldots; \, k_0 = k, \, \phi_0 = \phi).$$

It follows also that

$$F(k_n, \phi_n) = F(1, \Phi)$$

$$= \int_0^\Phi \frac{d\phi}{\sqrt{1 - \sin^2 \phi}} = \int_0^\Phi \sec \phi \, d\phi = \log_e \tan\left(\frac{\pi}{4} + \frac{\Phi}{2}\right)$$

and

$$F(k, \phi) = \sqrt{\frac{k_1 k_2 \ldots k_{n-1}}{k}} \, \log_e \tan\left(\frac{\pi}{4} + \frac{\Phi}{2}\right).$$

**Art. 46.** The method of the preceding articles may also be used to evaluate $F(30°, 40°)$, thus

$$
\begin{array}{ll}
k = .5 & \log k = 9.6989700 \\
1+k = 1.5 & \log (1+k) = 0.1760913
\end{array}
$$

$$
\begin{array}{r}
\log \sqrt{k} = 9.8494850 \\
\log 2 = 0.3010300 \\
\underline{\text{colog} (1+k) = 9.8239087} \\
\log k_1 = 9.9744237
\end{array}
$$

$$
\begin{array}{ll}
k_1 = .942809 & \log k_1 = 9.9744237 \\
1+k_1 = 1.942809 & \log (1+k_1) = 0.2884301
\end{array}
$$

$$
\begin{array}{r}
\log \sqrt{k_1} = 9.9872118 \\
\log 2 = 0.3010300 \\
\underline{\text{colog} (1+k_1) = 9.7115699} \\
\log k_2 = 9.9998117
\end{array}
$$

$$
\begin{array}{ll}
k_2 = .999567 & \log k_2 = 9.9998117 \\
1+k_2 = 1.999567 & \log (1+k_2) = 0.3009359
\end{array}
$$

$$
\begin{array}{r}
\log \sqrt{k_2} = 9.9999059 \\
\log 2 = 0.3010300 \\
\underline{\text{colog} (1+k_2) = 9.6990641} \\
\log k_3 = 0.0000000
\end{array}
$$

$k_3 = 1.$

$$
\begin{array}{r}
\log k = 9.6989700 \\
\underline{\log \sin \phi = 9.8080675} \\
\log \sin (2\phi_1 - \phi) = 9.5070375
\end{array}
$$

$$
\begin{array}{llll}
2\phi_1 - \phi = & 18° & 44' & 50.''05 \\
2\phi_1 = & 58° & 44' & 50.''10 \\
\phi_1 = & 29° & 22' & 25''.05
\end{array}
$$

$$\log k_1 = 9.99744237$$
$$\log \sin \phi_1 = 9.6906403$$

$$\log \sin (2\phi_2 - \phi_1) = 9.6650640$$

$$2\phi_2 - \phi_1 = 27° \quad 32' \quad 43.''08$$
$$2\phi_2 = 56° \quad 54' \quad 68.''13$$
$$\phi_2 = 28° \quad 27' \quad 34.''06$$

$$\log k_2 = 9.9998117$$
$$\log \sin \phi_2 = 9.6780866$$

$$\log \sin (2\phi_3 - \phi_2) = 9.6778983$$

$$2\phi_3 - \phi_2 = 28° \quad 26' \quad 45.''53$$
$$2\phi_3 = 56° \quad 54' \quad 19.''59$$
$$\phi_3 = 28° \quad 27' \quad 9.''78$$

When $k_3 = 1$, then $\sin (2\phi_4 - \phi_3) = \sin \phi_3$, or $\phi_4 = \phi_3$.

$$\therefore \phi_4 = 28° \quad 27' \quad 9.''78$$
$$\frac{\phi_4}{2} = 14° \quad 13' \quad 34.''89$$

$$\Phi = \frac{\phi_4}{2} + \frac{\pi}{4} = 59° \quad 13' \quad 34.''89$$

$$\Phi = 59° \quad 13' \quad 34.''89$$
$$\log_{10} \tan \Phi = .2251208$$
$$\log \log \tan \Phi = 9.3524156$$
$$\text{colog} M = 0.3622157 \text{ (*see below)}$$
$$\log \sqrt{k_1} = 9.9872118$$
$$\log \sqrt{k_2} = 9.9999059$$
$$\text{colog} \sqrt{k} = 0.1505150$$

$$\log F(30°, 40°) = 9.8522640$$
$$F(30°, 40°) = .711647. \ldots$$

**Art. 47.** Cayley, *Elliptic Functions*, p. 324, introduced instead of the standard form of the radical, a new form

$$\sqrt{a^2 \cos^2 \phi + b^2 \sin^2 \phi} \quad (a > b);$$

* Division is made by the modulus $M$ to change from the natural to the common logarithm, where $M = .43429448$.

and he further wrote

$$F(a, b, \phi) = \int_0^\phi \frac{d\phi}{\sqrt{a^2 \cos^2 \phi + b^2 \sin^2 \phi}}, \quad . \quad . \quad . \quad (1)$$

$$E(a, b, \phi) = \int_0^\phi \sqrt{a^2 \cos^2 \phi + b^2 \sin^2 \phi}. \quad . \quad . \quad . \quad (2)$$

It is clear that

$$\sqrt{a^2 \cos^2 \phi + b^2 \sin^2 \phi} = a\sqrt{1 - k^2 \sin^2 \phi},$$

where

$$k^2 = 1 - \frac{b^2}{a^2}, \ k' = \frac{b}{a}.$$

The functions (1) and (2) are consequently $\frac{1}{a}F(k, \phi)$ and $aE(k, \phi)$.

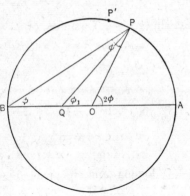

Fig. 17.

In the figure let $P$ be a point on the circle, whose centre is $O$ and let $Q$ be any point on the diameter $AB$.

Further let

$$QA = a, \ QB = b, \ \angle AQP = \phi_1, \ \angle AOP = 2\phi, \ \angle ABP = \phi.$$

Write $a_1 = \frac{1}{2}(a+b)$, $b_1 = \sqrt{ab}$, $c_1 = \frac{1}{2}(a-b)$.

It follows at once that

$$OA = OB = OP = a_1, \ OQ = a_1 - b = \frac{1}{2}(a-b) = c_1,$$

$$QP \sin \phi_1 = a_1 \sin 2\phi,$$

$$QP \cos \phi_1 = c_1 + a_1 \cos 2\phi.$$

On the other hand

$$\overline{QP}^2 = c_1{}^2 + 2c_1 a_1 \cos 2\phi + a_1{}^2 = \tfrac{1}{2}(a^2+b^2) + \tfrac{1}{2}(a^2-b^2) \cos 2\phi$$

$$= \tfrac{1}{2}(a^2+b^2)(\cos^2 \phi + \sin^2 \phi) + \tfrac{1}{2}(a^2-b^2)(\cos^2 \phi - \sin^2 \phi)$$

$$= a^2 \cos^2 \phi + b^2 \sin^2 \phi.$$

Therefore it follows that

$$\sin \phi_1 = \frac{a_1 \sin 2\phi}{\sqrt{a^2 \cos^2 \phi + b^2 \sin^2 \phi}}, \quad \cos \phi_1 = \frac{c_1 + a_1 \cos 2\phi}{\sqrt{a^2 \cos^2 \phi + b^2 \sin^2 \phi}};$$

and consequently

$$a_1{}^2 \cos^2 \phi_1 + b_1{}^2 \sin^2 \phi_1 = \frac{a_1{}^2(a \cos^2 \phi + b \sin^2 \phi)^2}{a^2 \cos^2 \phi + b^2 \sin^2 \phi}. \quad . \quad (\text{I})$$

It is seen at once that

$$\sin (2\phi - \phi_1) = \frac{\tfrac{1}{2}(a-b) \sin 2\phi}{\sqrt{a^2 \cos^2 \phi + b^2 \sin^2 \phi}},$$

$$\cos (2\phi - \phi_1) = \frac{a \cos^2 \phi + b \sin^2 \phi}{\sqrt{a^2 \cos^2 \phi + b^2 \sin^2 \phi}}; \text{ or, from } (\text{I}),$$

$$\cos (2\phi - \phi_1) = \frac{\text{I}}{a_1}\sqrt{a_1{}^2 \cos^2 \phi_1 + b_1{}^2 \sin^2 \phi_1}.$$

If in the figure we consider the point $P'$ consecutive to $P$, then, $\quad PQ \, d\phi_1 = PP' \sin PP'Q = 2a_1 \cos (2\phi - \phi_1)d\phi;$ or, writing for $PQ$ its value from above, there results

$$\frac{2d\phi}{\sqrt{a^2 \cos^2 \phi + b^2 \sin^2 \phi}} = \frac{d\phi_1}{\sqrt{a_1{}^2 \cos^2 \phi_1 + b_1{}^2 \sin^2 \phi_1}}.$$

Integrating, this expression becomes

$$F(a, b, \phi) = \tfrac{1}{2}F(a_1, b_1, \phi_1),$$

or

$$F(k, \phi) = \frac{\text{I}}{2}\frac{a}{a_1}F(k', \phi') = \frac{\text{I}}{\text{I}+k'}\, F(k_1, \phi_1),$$

where

$$\sin \phi_1 = \frac{\frac{1}{2}(1+k') \sin 2\phi}{\sqrt{1-k^2 \sin^2 \phi}}.$$

Note that $k^2 = 1 - \dfrac{b^2}{a^2}$, $k' = \dfrac{b}{a}$; $k_1{}^2 = 1 - \dfrac{b_1{}^2}{a_1{}^2} = \left(\dfrac{a-b}{a+b}\right)^2 = \left(\dfrac{1-k'}{1+k'}\right)^2$;

or, $k_1 = \dfrac{1-k'}{1+k'}$, and $k' = \dfrac{1-k_1}{1+k_1}$, as given at the end of Art. 42.

**Art. 48.** Cayley derives a similar formula for the integrals of the second kind as follows, his work being here in places considerably simplified. From the relation of Art. 42, we have

$$\sin (2\phi - \phi_1) = k_1 \sin \phi_1, \text{ or}$$

$$\sin 2\phi \cos \phi_1 - \cos 2\phi \sin \phi_1 = k_1 \sin \phi_1;$$

it follows that

$$\cos 2\phi = -k_1 \sin^2 \phi_1 + \cos \phi_1 \, \Delta\phi_1,$$

and consequently

$$2 \cos^2 \phi = 1 - k_1 \sin^2 \phi_1 + \cos \phi_1 \Delta\phi_1,$$

$$2 \sin^2 \phi = 1 + k_1 \sin^2 \phi_1 - \cos \phi_1 \Delta\phi_1.$$

From these two relations it is seen at once that

$$2 (a^2 \cos^2 \phi + b^2 \sin^2 \phi) = a^2 + b^2 - (a^2 - b^2) k_1 \sin^2 \phi_1$$

$$+ (a^2 - b^2) \cos \phi_1 \Delta\phi_1 = (a^2 + b^2)(\cos^2 \phi_1 + \sin^2 \phi_1)$$

$$- (a^2 - b^2) k_1 \sin^2 \phi_1 + (a^2 - b^2) \cos \phi_1 \Delta\phi_1$$

$$= 4(a_1{}^2 \cos^2 \phi_1 + b_1{}^2 \sin^2 \phi_1)$$

$$- 2b_1{}^2 + 4c_1 \cos \phi_1 \sqrt{a_1{}^2 \cos^2 \phi_1 + b_1{}^2 \sin^2 \phi_1}.$$

Multiply this expression by the differential relation given above, viz.,

$$\frac{2d\phi}{\sqrt{a^2 \cos^2 \phi + b^2 \sin^2 \phi}} = \frac{d\phi_1}{\sqrt{a_1{}^2 \cos^2 \phi_1 + b_1{}^2 \sin^2 \phi_1}},$$

and integrating, there results

$$E(a, b, \phi) = E(a_1, b_1, \phi_1) - \tfrac{1}{2}b_1^2 F(a_1, b_1, \phi_1) + c_1 \sin \phi_1,$$

where

$$\sin \phi_1 = \frac{a_1 \sin 2\phi}{\sqrt{a^2 \cos^2 \phi + b^2 \sin^2 \phi}}.$$

It follows at once that

$$E(k, \phi) = \frac{a_1}{a}E(k_1, \phi_1) - \frac{1}{2}\frac{b_1^2}{aa_1}F(k_1, \phi_1) + \frac{c_1}{a}\sin \phi_1,$$

or

$$E(k, \phi) = \frac{1}{2}(1+k')E(k_1, \phi_1) - \frac{k'}{1+k'}F(k_1, \phi_1) + \frac{1}{2}(1-k')\sin \phi_1,$$

with the initial relation

$$\sin (2\phi - \phi_1) = k_1 \sin \phi_1.$$

**.Art. 49.** From the formula connecting $\phi$ and $\phi_1$, which may be written in the form (see end of Art. 42)

$$\tan \phi_1 = \frac{(1+k') \tan \phi}{1 - k' \tan^2 \phi}, \quad \ldots \quad \ldots \quad (1)$$

it is seen that $\phi$ and $\phi_1$ vanish at the same time; and further since

$$\frac{d\phi'}{d\phi} = (1+k')\frac{1+k' \tan^2 \phi}{(1 - k' \tan^2 \phi)^2} \frac{\cos^2 \phi_1}{\cos^2 \phi},$$

a positive quantity, it appears that $\phi_1$ increases with $\phi$. It is further evident that $\tan \phi_1 = 0$ when $\tan \phi = \infty$. It is clear from (1) that when $\phi = 0$, $\phi_1 = 0$ and when $\tan \phi = \sqrt{\dfrac{1}{k'}} = \sqrt{\dfrac{a}{b}}$, then

$\phi_1 = \tfrac{1}{2}\pi$; and in general to the values $\dfrac{\pi}{2}$, $\pi$, $2\pi$, . . . of $\phi$, there correspond the values $\pi$, $2\pi$, $4\pi$, . . . . of $\phi_1$.

**Art. 50.** Denote the complete functions $F\left(a, b, \dfrac{\pi}{2}\right)$, $E\left(a, b, \dfrac{\pi}{2}\right)$

by $F(a, b,)$, $E(a, b)$, then

$$F(a, b) = \tfrac{1}{2}F(a_1, b_1, \pi) = F\left(a_1, b_1, \frac{\pi}{2}\right) = F(a_1, b_1);$$

and similarly

$$E(a, b) = 2E(a_1, b_1) - b_1^2 F(a_1, b_1).$$

**Art. 51.** *Continued repetition of the above transformations.* In the same manner as $a_1$, $b_1$, $c_1$ were derived from $a$, $b$, we may derive $a_2$, $b_2$, $c_2$ from $a_1$, $b_1$, etc., and thus form the following table:

$$a_1 = \tfrac{1}{2}(a+b), \qquad b_1 = \sqrt{ab}, \qquad c_1 = \tfrac{1}{2}(a-b),$$
$$a_2 = \tfrac{1}{2}(a_1+b_1), \qquad b_2 = \sqrt{a_1 b_1}, \qquad c_2 = \tfrac{1}{2}(a_1-b_1),$$
$$a_3 = \tfrac{1}{2}(a_2+b_2), \qquad b_3 = \sqrt{a_2 b_2}, \qquad c_3 = \tfrac{1}{2}(a_2-b_2),$$

$$\cdot \qquad \cdot \qquad \cdot \qquad \cdot \qquad \cdot$$

Note that $a_1 - b_1 = \dfrac{(\sqrt{a} - \sqrt{b})^2}{2}$ and that

$$a_2 - b_2 = \frac{a_1+b_1}{2} - \sqrt{a_1 b_1} = \frac{a_1-b_1}{2} - [\sqrt{a_1} - \sqrt{b_1}]\sqrt{b_1},$$

so that

$$a_2 - b_2 < \frac{a_1-b_1}{2} \quad \text{or} \quad a_2 - b_2 < \frac{(\sqrt{a} - \sqrt{b})^2}{2^2}.$$

Similarly it is seen that $a_3 - b_3 < \dfrac{a_2-b_2}{2} < \dfrac{(\sqrt{a} - \sqrt{b})^3}{2^3}$; and in general $a_n - b_n < \dfrac{(\sqrt{a} - \sqrt{b})^n}{2^n}$, or $\lim (a_n - b_n) = 0$. It is clear that as $n$ increases $a_n$ and $b_n$ approach (very rapidly) one and the same limit, which is called[*] by Gauss the *arithmetico-geometrical mean* and denoted by him with the symbol $M(a, b) = \mu$. However, when $a_n = b_n$, then

$$F(a_n, b_n, \phi) = \frac{\phi}{a_n} \text{and } E(a_n, b_n, \phi) = a_n\phi;$$

[*] Gauss, *Werke*, III, pp. 361–404.

further if $\phi = \frac{1}{2}\pi$, it is seen that

$$F(a_n, b_n) = \frac{\pi}{2a_n} \text{ and } E(a_n, b_n) = \frac{\pi}{2} a_n, \text{ where } a_n = \mu.$$

The equation $F(a, b, \phi) = \frac{1}{2} F(a_1, b_1, \phi_1)$ gives

$$F(a, b, \phi) = \frac{1}{2}F(a_1, b_1, \phi_1) = \frac{1}{2^2} F(a_2, b_2, \phi_2)$$

$$= \ldots = \frac{1}{2^n} F(a_n, b_n, \phi_n) = \frac{1}{2^n a_n} \phi_n,$$

where the $\phi$'s are to be calculated from the formula

$$\sin \phi_1 = \frac{a_1 \sin 2\phi}{\sqrt{a^2 \cos^2 \phi + b^2 \sin^2 \phi}},$$

$$\sin \phi_2 = \frac{a_2 \sin 2\phi_1}{\sqrt{a_1^2 \cos^2 \phi_1 + b_1^2 \sin^2 \phi_1}}, \ldots$$

**Art. 52.** *The integrals of the second kind.* Note that, since

$$F(a, b, \phi) = \frac{1}{2}F(a_1, b_1, \phi_1),$$

the formula above for the $E$-function may be written

$$E(a, b, \phi) - a^2 F(a, b, \phi) = E(a_1, b_1, \phi_1) - a_1^2 F(a_1, b_1, \phi_1)$$

$$+ F(a_1, b_1, \phi_1)(a_1^2 - \tfrac{1}{2}a^2 - \tfrac{1}{2}b_1^2) + c_1 \sin \phi_1;$$

or, since $a_1^2 - \tfrac{1}{2}a^2 - \tfrac{1}{2}b_1^2 = -\tfrac{1}{4}(a^2 - b^2) = -a_1 c_1$,

the above equation is

$$E(a, b, \phi) - a^2 F(a, b, \phi) = E(a_1, b_1, \phi_1) - a_1^2 F(a_1, b_1, \phi_1)$$

$$- a_1 c_1 F(a_1, b_1, \phi_1) + c_1 \sin \phi_1.$$

Observing that, as $n$ increases,

$$\lim [E(a_n, b_n, \phi_n) - a_n^2 F(a_n, b_n, \phi_n)] = 0,$$

it is seen that

$$E(a, b, \phi) - a^2 F(a, b, \phi) = -[2a_1 c_1 + 4a_2 c_2 + 8a_3 c_3 + \ldots]F(a, b, \phi)$$

$$+ c_1 \sin \phi_1 + c_2 \sin \phi_2 + c_3 \sin \phi_3 + \ldots;$$

or finally

$$E(a, b, \phi) = [a^2 - 2a_1 c_1 - 4a_2 c_2 - 8a_3 c_3 - \ldots]F(a, b, \phi)$$

$$+ c_1 \sin \phi_1 + c_2 \sin \phi_2 + c_3 \sin \phi_3 + \ldots$$

In particular, if $\phi = \frac{1}{2}\pi$, we have Art. 49, $\phi_1 = \pi$, $\phi_2 = 2\pi$, . . . , and then

$$E(a, b) = [a^2 - 2a_1c_1 - 4a_2c_2 - \ \cdots \ ]\frac{\pi}{2a_n}.$$

It also follows immediately that

$$E(k, \phi) = \left[ 1 - \frac{2a_1c_1}{a^2} - \frac{4a_2c_2}{a^2} - \ \cdots \ \right] F(k, \phi)$$

$$+ \frac{c_1}{a}\sin \phi_1 + \frac{c_2}{a}\sin \phi_2 + \frac{c_3}{a}\sin \phi_3 + \ \cdots \ ;$$

or, noting that

$$\frac{a_1c_1}{a_2} = \frac{1}{4} k^2, \ \frac{a_2c_2}{a_1c_1} = \frac{1}{4} k_1, \ \frac{a_3c_3}{a_2c_2} = \frac{1}{4} k_2, \ \cdots \ ,$$

$$\frac{c_1}{a} = \frac{k_1}{1+k_1},$$

$$\frac{c_2}{a_1} = \frac{k_2}{1+k_2}, \ \frac{a_1}{a} = \frac{1}{1+k_1},$$

$$\frac{c_3}{a_2} = \frac{k_3}{1+k_3}, \ \frac{a_2}{a_1} = \frac{1}{1+k_2}, \ \frac{a_1}{a} = \frac{1}{1+k_1}, \ \cdots \ ,$$

the equation becomes,

$$E(k, \phi) = [1 - \tfrac{1}{2}k^2(1 + \tfrac{1}{2}k_1 + \tfrac{1}{4}k_1k_2 + \tfrac{1}{8}k_1k_2k_3 + \ \cdots \ )]F(k, \phi)$$

$$+ \frac{k_1}{1+k_1}\sin \phi_1 + \frac{k_2}{(1+k_1)(1+k_2)}\sin \phi_2$$

$$+ \frac{k_3}{(1+k_1)(1+k_2)(1+k_3)}\sin \phi_3 + \ \cdots \ .$$

Further since

$$\frac{1}{1+k_1} = \frac{k}{2\sqrt{k_1}}, \ \text{or} \ \frac{1}{1+k_1} = \frac{k}{2\sqrt{k_1}},$$

$$\frac{1}{1+k_2} = \frac{k_1}{2\sqrt{k_2}}, \ \text{or} \ \frac{1}{(1+k_1)(1+k_2)} = \frac{k\sqrt{k_1}}{4\sqrt{k_2}},$$

$$\frac{1}{1+k_3} = \frac{k_2}{2\sqrt{k_3}}, \ \text{or} \ \frac{1}{(1+k_1)(1+k_2)(1+k_3)} = \frac{k\sqrt{k_1k_2}}{8\sqrt{k_3}},$$

$$. \qquad . \qquad . \qquad . \qquad . \qquad . \qquad .$$

the last line of the above expression may be written

$$k[\tfrac{1}{2}\sqrt{k_1}\,\sin\phi_1 + \tfrac{1}{4}\sqrt{k_1 k_2}\,\sin\phi_2 + \tfrac{1}{8}\sqrt{k_1 k_2 k_3}\,\sin\phi_3 + \ldots].$$

In particular if $\phi = \tfrac{1}{2}\pi$, we have

$$E_1 = E\left(k, \frac{\pi}{2}\right) = [1 - \tfrac{1}{2}k^2(1 + \tfrac{1}{2}k_1 + \tfrac{1}{4}k_1 k_2 + \tfrac{1}{8}k_1 k_2 k_3 + \ldots]F_1(k).$$

**Art. 53.** As a numerical example (see Legendre, *Traité* etc., T. I, p. 91), let $a = 1$, $b = \tfrac{1}{2}\sqrt{2 - \sqrt{3}} = \cos 75°$, and let $\tan\phi = \sqrt{\dfrac{2}{\sqrt{3}}}$.

It follows that $k^2 = 1 - \dfrac{b^2}{a^2} = \sin 75°$.

The following table may be at once constructed.

| Index | $a$ | $b$ | $c$ | $k$ | $k'$ | $\phi$ | | |
|-------|-----|-----|-----|-----|------|---|---|---|
| | | | | | | ° | ′ | ″ |
| (0) | 1.0000000 | 0.2588190 | ........ | 0.9659258 | 0.2588190 | 47 | 3 | 31 |
| (1) | 0.6294095 | 0.5087426 | 0.3705905 | 0.5887908 | 0.8082856 | 62 | 36 | 3 |
| (2) | 0.5690761 | 0.5658688 | 0.0603334 | 0.1060200 | 0.9943636 | 119 | 55 | 48 |
| (3) | 0.5674724 | 0.5674701 | 0.0016037 | 0.0028260 | 0.9999959 | 240 | 0 | 0 |
| (4) | 0.5674713 | 0.5674713 | 0.0000011 | 0.0000020 | 0.9999999 | 480 | 0 | 0 |

(See Cayley, loc. cit., p. 335.)

The complete integral $F_1 = \dfrac{\pi}{2}\dfrac{1}{a_4} = 2.768063 \ldots$ and

$$F(75°,\ 47°\ 3'\ 31'') = \frac{\phi_4}{8} \cdot \frac{1}{a_4} = 0.9226877 \ldots$$

Note that the first integral is *three times* the second.
It is also seen that

$$\tfrac{1}{2}\left(1 - \frac{E_1}{F_1}\right) = \quad a_1 c_1 = .2332532$$

$$+ 2a_2 c_2 = .0686686$$

$$+ 4a_3 c_3 = .0036402$$

$$+ 8a_4 c_4 = .0000051$$

$$\overline{\phantom{+ 8a_4 c_4 }}$$

$$= .3055671$$

and $E_1 = 1.0764051 \ldots$

The computation of $E(k, \phi)$ is found in the next article.

**Art. 54.** To establish in a somewhat different manner the results that were given in the preceding article, consider * a function $G(k, \phi)$ composed of an integral of the first and of an integral of the second kind, such that

$$G(k, \phi) = \int_0^\phi \frac{\alpha + \beta \sin^2 \phi}{\sqrt{1 - k^2 \sin^2 \phi}} d\phi,$$

where $\alpha$ and $\beta$ are constants.

Making in this integral the substitutions of Arts. 42 and 48, namely

$$\frac{d\phi}{\Delta\phi} = \frac{1+k_1}{2} \frac{d\phi_1}{\Delta\phi_1}, \quad \sin^2 \phi = \tfrac{1}{2}(1 + k_1 \sin^2 \phi_1 - \Delta\phi_1 \cos \phi_1),$$

it is seen that

$$G(k, \phi) = \frac{1+k_1}{2}[G(k_1, \phi_1) - \tfrac{1}{2}\beta \sin \phi_1], \quad \ldots \quad (1)$$

where

$$G(k_1, \phi_1) = \int_0^{\phi_1} \frac{\alpha_1 + \beta_1 \sin^2 \phi_1}{\Delta\phi_1} d\phi_1,$$

the constants $\alpha_1$ and $\beta_1$ being defined by the relations

$$\alpha_1 = \alpha + \tfrac{1}{2}\beta, \ \beta_1 = \tfrac{1}{2}\beta k_1.$$

We saw in Art. 48 that

$$k_1 = \frac{1 - \sqrt{1 - k^2}}{1 + \sqrt{1 - k^2}}, \quad \tan(\phi_1 - \phi) = \sqrt{1 - k^2} \tan \phi,$$

where $k_1 < k$ and $\phi_1 > \phi$.

It follows directly from (1) that

$$G(k, \phi) = \frac{1+k_1}{2} \cdot \frac{1+k_2}{2} \ldots \frac{1+k_n}{2} G(k_n, \phi_n)$$

$$- \frac{1}{2}\left[ \frac{1+k_1}{2}\beta \sin \phi_1 + \frac{1+k_1}{2} \cdot \frac{1+k_2}{2}\beta_1 \sin \phi_2 + \ldots \right.$$

$$\left. + \frac{1+k_1}{2} \cdot \frac{1+k_2}{2} \ldots \frac{1+k_n}{2}\beta_{n-1} \sin \phi_n \right],$$

---

* See also Legendre, *Traité*, etc., I, p. 108.

where

$$\beta_p = \beta \frac{k_1 k_2 \ldots k_p}{2^p},$$

and

$$\alpha_p = \alpha + \tfrac{1}{2}\beta \left( 1 + \frac{k_1}{2} + \frac{k_1 k_2}{2^2} + \ldots + \frac{k_1 k_2 \ldots k_{p-1}}{2^{p-1}} \right).$$

Since $\beta_n$ becomes $0$ with $k_n$, it is seen that

$$\lim_{n=\infty} G(k_n, \phi_n) = \int_0^{\phi_n} \alpha_n \, d\phi = \alpha_n \phi_n.$$

From Art. 43 we had

$$\frac{1+k_1}{2} \cdot \frac{1+k_2}{2} \ldots \frac{1+k_n}{2} \phi_n = F(k, \phi),$$

and, see Art. 42,

$$\frac{1+k_1}{2} = \frac{\sqrt{k_1}}{k}, \quad \frac{1+k_2}{2} = \frac{\sqrt{k_2}}{k_1}, \quad \ldots .$$

It follows that the above formula becomes

$$G(k, \phi) = F(k, \phi) \left[ \alpha + \tfrac{1}{2}\beta \left( 1 + \frac{k_1}{2} + \frac{k_1 k_2}{2^2} + \frac{k_1 k_2 k_3}{2^3} + \ldots \right) \right]$$

$$- \frac{\beta}{k} \left( \frac{\sqrt{k_1}}{2} \sin \phi_1 + \frac{\sqrt{k_1 k_2}}{2^2} \sin \phi_2 + \frac{\sqrt{k_1 k_2 k_3}}{2^3} \sin \phi_3 + \ldots \right).$$

If in this formula we put $\alpha = 1$, $\beta = -k^2$, it becomes

$$E(k, \phi) = F(k, \phi) \left[ 1 - \frac{k^2}{2} \left( 1 + \frac{k_1}{2} + \frac{k_1 k_2}{2^2} + \frac{k_1 k_2 k_3}{2^3} + \ldots \right) \right]$$

$$+ k \left[ \frac{\sqrt{k_1}}{2} \sin \phi_1 + \frac{\sqrt{k_1 k_2}}{2^2} \sin \phi_2 + \frac{\sqrt{k_1 k_2 k_3}}{2^3} \sin \phi_3 + \ldots \right],$$

where

$$k_p = \frac{1 - \sqrt{1 - k^2_{p-1}}}{1 + \sqrt{1 - k^2_{p-1}}}$$

and

$$\tan (\phi_p - \phi_{p-1}) = \sqrt{1 - k^2_{p-1}} \tan \phi_{p-1}.$$

These results verify those of Art. 52.

With Legendre, *Fonct. Ellip.*, T. I., p. 114, we may find $E(k, \phi)$ where $k = \sin 75°$ and $\tan \phi = \sqrt{\dfrac{2}{\sqrt{3}}}$.

Using the results of Art. 53 it is seen that

$$\frac{k\sqrt{k_1}}{2} \sin \phi_1 = .3290186$$

$$\frac{k\sqrt{k_1 k_2}}{4} \sin \phi_2 = .0522872$$

$$\frac{k\sqrt{k_1 k_2 k_3}}{8} \sin \phi_3 = -.0013888$$

$$\frac{k\sqrt{k_1 k_2 k_3 k_4}}{16} \sin \phi_4 = .0000010$$

$$\text{sum} = .3799180$$

Writing

$$L = 1 - \frac{k^2}{2} - \frac{k^2 k_1}{4} - \frac{k^2 k_1 k_2}{8} - \frac{k^2 k_1 k_2 k_3}{16},$$

it is found that $L = .3888658 \ldots$

In Art. 53 it was seen that $F(k, \phi) = .9226877 \ldots$

It follows that $E(k, \phi) = F(k, \phi)L + .3799180 \ldots = 0.7387196 \ldots$

Further since

$$E\left(k, \frac{\pi}{2}\right) = F\left(k, \frac{\pi}{2}\right)L,$$

there follows

$$E_1 = 1.0764049 \ldots$$

**Art. 55.** *Inverse order of transformation.* If the modulus $k$ is nearer unity than zero, the following method is preferable. The equation (1) of the preceding article may be written

$$G(k_1, \phi_1) = \frac{2}{1+k_1} G(k, \phi) + \frac{\beta_1}{k_1} \sin \phi_1, \text{ since } \frac{\beta_1}{k_1} = \frac{\beta}{2}.$$

If in this formula the suffixes be interchanged, then

$$G(k, \phi) = \frac{2}{1+k} G(k_1, \phi_1) + \frac{\beta}{k} \sin \phi,$$

where now

$$\beta_1 = \frac{2\beta}{k}, \quad \alpha_1 = \alpha - \frac{\beta}{k},$$

$$k_1 = \frac{2\sqrt{k}}{1+k}, \quad \sin(2\phi_1 - \phi) = k \sin \phi,$$

$$k_1 > k, \quad \phi_1 < \phi.$$

The continued repetition of (2) gives

$$G(k, \phi) = \frac{\beta}{k} \sin \phi + \frac{\beta_1}{\sqrt{k}} \sin \phi_1 + \frac{\sqrt{k_1}}{\sqrt{k}} \beta_2 \sin \phi_2$$

$$+ \frac{\sqrt{k_1 k_2}}{\sqrt{k}} \beta_3 \sin \phi_3 + \frac{\sqrt{k_1 k_2 \ldots k_{n-2}}}{\sqrt{k}} \beta_{n-1} \sin \phi_{n-1}$$

$$+ k_n \frac{\sqrt{k_1 k_2 \ldots k_{n-1}}}{\sqrt{k}} G(k_n, \phi_n),$$

where

$$\beta_p = \frac{2^p \beta}{k k_1 \ldots k_{p-1}},$$

and

$$\alpha_p = \alpha - \frac{\beta}{k}\left(1 + \frac{2}{k_1} + \frac{2^2}{k_1 k_2} + \ldots + \frac{2^{p-1}}{k_1 k_2 \ldots k_{p-1}}\right).$$

Since $k_n$ approaches unity (rapidly) as $n$ increases,

$$\lim_n G(k_n, \phi_n) = \int_0^{\phi_n} \frac{\alpha_n + \beta_n \sin^2 \phi}{\cos \phi} d\phi$$

$$= (\alpha_n + \beta_n) \log_e \tan\left(\frac{\pi}{4} + \frac{\phi_n}{2}\right) - \beta_n \sin \phi_n.$$

In Art. 45 it was shown that

$$\lim k_n \sqrt{\frac{k_1 k_2 \ldots k_{n-1}}{k}} \log \tan\left(\frac{\pi}{4} + \frac{\phi_n}{2}\right) = F(k, \phi).$$

We may consequently write the above formula

$$G(k, \phi) = F(k, \phi)\left[\alpha - \frac{\beta}{k}\left(1 + \frac{2}{k_1} + \frac{2^2}{k_1 k_2} + \ldots + \frac{2^{n-1} - 2^n}{k_1 k_2 \ldots k_{n-1}}\right)\right]$$

$$+ \frac{\beta}{k}\left[\sin\phi + \frac{2}{\sqrt{k}}\sin\phi_1 + \frac{2^2}{\sqrt{kk_1}}\sin\phi_2 + \frac{2^3}{\sqrt{kk_1k_2}}\sin\phi_3 + \ldots\right.$$

$$\left. + \frac{2^{n-1}}{\sqrt{kk_1 \ldots k_{n-2}}}\sin\phi_{n-1} - \frac{2^n}{\sqrt{kk_1 \ldots k_{n-1}}}\sin\phi_n\right].$$

Writing $\alpha = 1$, $\beta = -k^2$ in this formula, it becomes

$$E(k, \phi) = F(k, \phi)\left[1 + k\left(1 + \frac{2}{k_1} + \frac{2^2}{k_1 k_2} + \ldots\right.\right.$$

$$\left.\left. + \frac{2^{n-1}}{k_1 k_2 \ldots k_{n-1}} - \frac{2^n}{k_1 k_2 \ldots k_{n-1}}\right)\right]$$

$$- k\left(\sin\phi + \frac{2}{\sqrt{k}}\sin\phi_1 + \frac{2^2}{\sqrt{kk_1}}\sin\phi_2 + \ldots\right.$$

$$\left. + \frac{2^{n-1}}{\sqrt{kk_1 k_2 \ldots k_{n-2}}}\sin\phi_{n-1} - \frac{2^n}{\sqrt{kk_1 \ldots k_{n-1}}}\sin\phi_n\right),$$

where

$$k_p = \frac{2\sqrt{k_{p-1}}}{1 + k_{p-1}} \text{ and } \sin(2\phi_p - \phi_{p-1}) = k_{p-1}\sin\phi_{p-1}.$$

Taking the example of the preceding article, and using the values given in Art. 53, it is seen that

$$-k\sin\phi = -0.7071070$$

$$-2\sqrt{k}\sin\phi_1 = -1.4146540$$

$$+4\frac{\sqrt{k}}{\sqrt{k_1}}\sin\phi_2 = \quad 2.8293085$$

$$F(k, \phi) = .9226877$$

and

$$F(k, \phi)\left[1 + k - \frac{2k}{k_1}\right] = \quad 0.0311720$$

$$E(k, \phi) = \quad 0.7387195 \ldots$$

**Art. 56.** Two of the principal problems that appear in practice will now be given.

PROBLEM 1. *When u and k are given, calculate the values of sn u, cn u, dn u.*

1. Computation of *sn u*. In the Table II, p. 96, is found an immediate answer to the problem.

For when $u$ and $k = \sin \theta$ are known, the value $\phi$ may be found in the table and then *sn u* from the formula $sn\ u = \sin \phi$.

If, for example, $k = \frac{1}{2} = \sin \theta$, and $u = .47551$, it is seen that for $\theta = 30°$, $u = .47551$, we have $\phi = 27°$, and $\sin \phi = .45399 = sn\ u$.

2. The computation of *cn u* and *dn u* are had from the formulas

$$cn\ u = \pm \sqrt{(1 - sn\ u)(1 + sn\ u)},$$

$$dn\ u = \pm \sqrt{(1 - ksn\ u)(1 + ksn\ u)}.$$

PROBLEM 2. *Having given the elliptic function, calculate the argument.*

1. If *sn u* is known, find *u*. Table II furnishes the solution. Suppose that $a$ is the given value of *sn u*, and suppose that $k = \sin \theta$ is also known. Hence, since $sn\ u = \sin \phi = a$, we may determine $\phi$. With $\theta$ and $\phi$ known, we find the value of $u$ from the table. Denote this value by $u_0$. From the relation $sn\ u = sn\ u_0$, we have (Art. 21),

$$u = u_0 + 4mK + 2m'iK'.$$

Further in the formula (Art. 12).

$$sn\ u = -sn(u + 2K),$$

substitute $u = -u_0$, and then we have $-sn\ u_0 = -sn(2K - u_0)$, so that $u$ may also have the form

$$u = 2K - u_0 + 4mK + 2m'iK'.$$

2. If *cn u* and *dn u* are given, *snu* and then *u* may be found as above.

# CHAPTER V

## MISCELLANEOUS EXAMPLES AND PROBLEMS

1. *The rectification of the lemniscate.* The equation of the curve is

$$(y^2+x^2)^2+a^2(y^2-x^2)=0;$$

or, writing $x=r \cos \theta$, $y=r \sin \theta$, the equation becomes

$$r^2=a^2 \cos 2\theta.$$

From the expression $ds^2=dr^2+r^2d\theta^2$, the differential of arc is

$$ds=\mp\frac{dr}{\sqrt{1-\dfrac{r^4}{a^4}}}=\mp\frac{ad\theta}{\sqrt{1-2 \sin^2 \theta}}.$$

Writing, see **II** of Art. 3, $r=a \cos \phi$, so that $2 \sin^2 \theta=\sin \phi$, it is seen that

$$s=a\int_0^\theta \frac{d\theta}{\sqrt{1-2 \sin^2 \theta}}=\frac{a}{\sqrt{2}}\int_0^\phi \frac{d\phi}{\sqrt{1-\frac{1}{2} \sin^2 \phi}}=\frac{a}{\sqrt{2}} F\left(\frac{1}{\sqrt{2}}, \phi\right),$$

which may be calculated at once from the tables when $a$ and $\theta$ (or $\phi$) are given. A quadrant of the lemniscate is

$$S_q=a\int_0^{\frac{\pi}{4}} \frac{d\theta}{\sqrt{1-2 \sin^2 \theta}}=\frac{a}{\sqrt{2}}\int_0^{\frac{\pi}{2}} \frac{d\phi}{\sqrt{1-\frac{1}{2} \sin^2 \phi}}=\frac{a}{\sqrt{2}} K\left(\frac{1}{\sqrt{2}}\right).$$

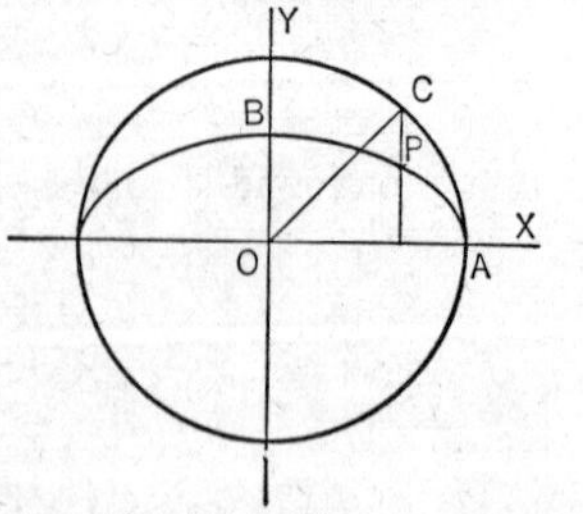

2. *The rectification of the ellipse.*

Let the equation be $\dfrac{x^2}{a^2}+\dfrac{y^2}{b^2}=1$, $a>b$ .

From the integral

$$s=\int_0^x \sqrt{1+\left(\frac{dy}{dx}\right)^2}\,dx,$$

we have, by writing $k^2=\dfrac{a^2-b^2}{a^2}$, $x=a\,t$,

$$s=a\int_0^t \frac{(1-k^2t^2)dt}{\sqrt{(1-t^2)(1-k^2t^2)}}.$$

FIG. 18.

Finally writing $t=\sin \phi$ (see Art. 3) and that is $x=a \sin \phi$, we have

$$s=\int_0^\phi \Delta\phi\, d\phi=aE(\phi).$$

Here $k$ is the *numerical eccentricity* of the ellipse. The angle $\phi = COY = 90 - COA$, where in astronomy the angle $COA$ is known as the eccentric anomaly of the point $P$. Writing $\phi = \pi/2$, it is seen that the quadrant of the ellipse is $aE$, where $E$ is the *complete* integral of the second kind.

If the equation of the ellipse is taken in the form

$$x = a \sin \phi, \quad y = b \cos \phi,$$

it follows at once that

$$ds^2 = a^2(1 - k^2 \sin^2 \phi)d\phi^2, \quad \text{or} \quad s = aE(\phi).$$

3. The major and minor axes of an ellipse are 100 and 50 centimeters respectively. Find the length of the arc between the points $(0, 25)$ and $(48, 7)$. Find also the length of the arc between the points $(48, 7)$ and $(50, 0)$. Determine the length of its quadrant.

4. If $\lambda$ denotes the latitude of a point $P$ on the earth's surface, the equation of the ellipse through this point as indicated in the figure, may be written in the form

$$x = \frac{a \cos \lambda}{\sqrt{1 - e^2 \sin^2 \lambda}}, \quad y = \frac{a(1 - e^2) \sin \lambda}{\sqrt{1 - e^2 \sin^2 \lambda}}.$$

It follows at once that

$$ds^2 = dx^2 + dy^2 = \frac{a^2(1 - e^2)^2 d\lambda^2}{(1 - e^2 \sin^2 \lambda)^3},$$

so that

$$s = a(1 - e^2) \int_0^\lambda \frac{d\lambda}{(1 - e^2 \sin^2 \lambda)}.$$

This integral may be at once evaluated by the third formula in Art. 41.

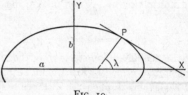

Fig. 19.

Compute the lengths of arc of the ellipse between $10°$ and $11°$ and between $79°$ and $80°$ where $a = 6378278$ meters and $e^2 = 0.0067686$. Compare these distances with the length of an arc that subtends $1°$ upon a circle with radius $= 6378278$ meters.

5. Plot the curves, the *elastic curves*, which are defined through the differential equation

$$d\phi = \pm \frac{y^2 dy}{\sqrt{a^4 - y^4}},$$

for the values $a = 1, 2, 4, 9$.

6. The axes of two right cylinders of radii $a$ and $b$ respectively $(a > b)$ intersect at right angles. Find the volume common to both.

Let the $z$-axis be that of the larger cylinder and the $y$-axis that of the smaller, so that the equations of the cylinders are

$$x^2 + y^2 = a^2 \quad \text{and} \quad x^2 + z^2 = b^2 \quad \text{respectively.}$$

The volume in question is

$$V = 8 \int_0^b \sqrt{a^2 - x^2} \, \sqrt{b^2 - x^2} \, dx.$$

Writing $t = sn^{-1}\left(\dfrac{x}{b}, \dfrac{b}{a}\right)$, (see formula 5a, Art. 23), then $x = b \, sn \, t, \, b^2 - x^2 = b^2 cn^2 t, \, a^2 - x^2 = a^2 dn^2 t, \, d\phi = b \, cn \, t \, dn \, t \, dt$.

It follows that

$$V = 8ab^2 \int_0^K \left[ 1 - \frac{a^2 + b^2}{a^2} sn^2 t + \frac{b^2}{a^2} sn^4 t \right] dt. \quad \text{(See Byerly, } Int.\,Cal.,\, 1902, \text{p. 276.)}$$

Noting (see sixth formula of Art. 41, and (ii) of Art. 48) that

$$\int_0^K sn^2 t \, dt = \frac{1}{k^2}[K - E] \text{ and } 3k^4 \int_0^K sn^4 t \, dt = 2K - 2E + k^2 K - 2k^2 E, \ k^2 = \frac{b^2}{a^2},$$

it follows at once that

$$V = \tfrac{8}{3}a[(a^2 + b^2)E - (a^2 - b^2)K].$$

Compute $V$ when $a = 60$ and $b = 12$ centimeters respectively; also find the volume common to both when the shortest distance between the axes is 8 centimeters.

7. The differential equation of motion of the simple pendulum is

$$\frac{d^2 s}{dt^2} = -g \frac{dy}{ds};$$

or multiplying by $\dfrac{2ds}{dt}$ and integrating,

$$\left(\frac{ds}{dt}\right)^2 = -2gy + C.$$

If the pendulum bob starts from the lowest point of its circular path with the initial velocity that would be acquired by a particle falling freely in a vacuum through the distance $y_0$, so that $v_0^2 = 2gy_0$ (Byerly, loc. cit., p. 215), it is seen that this is the value of $C$, and consequently

$$\left(\frac{ds}{dt}\right)^2 = 2g(y_0 - y).$$

Further taking the starting-point as the origin (see figure) the equation of the circular path is $x^2 + y^2 - 2ay = 0$, so that

$$\left(\frac{ds}{dt}\right)^2 = \frac{a^2}{2ay - y^2}\left(\frac{dy}{dt}\right)^2,$$

and consequently

$$t = \frac{a}{\sqrt{2g}} \int_0^y \frac{dy}{\sqrt{(y_0 - y)(2ay - y^2)}},$$

which is the time required to reach that point of the path whose ordinate is $y$.

Writing $k^2 = \dfrac{y_0}{2a}$ and $\sin^2 \phi = \dfrac{y}{y_0}$, this integral becomes at once

$$t = \sqrt{\frac{a}{g}} \int_0^\phi \frac{d\phi}{\sqrt{1 - k^2 \sin^2 \phi}} = \sqrt{\frac{a}{g}} \, F(k, \phi).$$

Let $OC = CA = a$ be the length of the pendulum. Let $A$ be the highest point reached by it in the oscillation so that the ordinate of $A$ is $y_0$. Let the angle $ACO$ be $\alpha$, and let $\theta$ be the angle $PCO$, where $P$ is the point reached at the expiration of the time $t$.

It is seen that

$$\frac{y_0}{a} = 1 - \cos \alpha,$$

so that

$$\sqrt{\frac{y_0}{2a}} = \sqrt{\tfrac{1}{2}(1 - \cos \alpha)} = \sin \frac{\alpha}{2} = k;$$

and similarly,

$$\sqrt{\frac{y}{2a}} = \sin \frac{\theta}{2}.$$

It follows also that

$$\sin \phi = \sqrt{\frac{g}{y_0}} = \frac{\sin \dfrac{\theta}{2}}{\sin \dfrac{\alpha}{2}}.$$

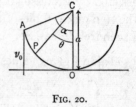

Fig. 20.

When $\theta = \alpha$, $\sin \phi = 1$, or $\phi = \dfrac{\pi}{2}$, and consequently, the time of a half-oscillation is $\sqrt{\dfrac{a}{g}}\, F\left(\sin \dfrac{\alpha}{2}, \dfrac{\pi}{2}\right)$.

Show by Table I that when $a = 36°$, the time of oscillation is $1.0253 \ldots$ times greater than that given by the approximate formula $t = \sqrt{\dfrac{a}{g}}\, \pi$.

The following problems taken from Byerly's Calculus are instructive:

8. A pendulum swings through an angle of $180°$; required, the time of oscillation. *Ans.* $3.708 \sqrt{\dfrac{a}{g}}$.

9. The time of vibration of a pendulum swinging in an arc of $72°$ is observed to be 2 seconds; how long does it take it to fall through an arc of $5°$, beginning at a point $20°$ from the highest point of the arc of swing? *Ans.* $0.095 \ldots$ second.

10. A pendulum for which $\sqrt{\dfrac{a}{g}}$ is $\tfrac{1}{2}$, vibrates through an arc of $180°$; through what arc does it rise in the first half second after it has passed its lowest point? In the first $\tfrac{1}{8}$ of a second? *Ans.* $69°$; $20° \, 6'$.

11. Show that a pendulum which beats seconds when swinging through an angle of $6°$, will lose 11 to 12 seconds a day if made to swing through $8°$ and 26 seconds a day if made to swing through $10°$.

(Simpson's *Fluxions*, § 464.)

## CHAPTER VI

### FIVE-PLACE TABLES

THE following tables of integrals are given in Levy's *Théorie des fonctions elliptiques*. As stated by Professor Levy, he was assisted by Professor G. Humbert in compiling these tables from the ten-place tables that are found in the second volume of Legendre's Treatise.

Table I gives values of the integrals

$$K = \int_0^{\frac{1}{2}\pi} \frac{d\phi}{\sqrt{1 - \sin^2 \theta \sin^2 \phi}} \quad \text{and} \quad E = \int_0^{\frac{1}{2}\pi} d\phi \sqrt{1 - \sin^2 \theta \sin^2 \phi}.$$

For example, if $\theta = 78° 30'$, then $K = 3.01918$ and $E = 1.05024$.

Table II gives values of the integral

$$F(k, \phi) = \int_0^{\phi} \frac{d\phi}{\sqrt{1 - \sin^2 \theta \sin^2 \phi}}.$$

For example, if $\theta = 65°$ and $\phi = 81°$, then $F(k,\phi) = 1.94377$.

Table III gives values of the integral

$$E(k, \phi) = \int_0^{\phi} d\phi \sqrt{1 - \sin^2 \theta \sin^2 \phi}.$$

For example, if $\theta = 40°$ and $\phi = 34°$, then $E(k, \phi) = 0.57972$.

## I.—THE COMPLETE ELLIPTIC INTEGRALS OF THE FIRST AND SECOND KINDS

| θ | K | E | θ | K | E | θ | K | E |
|---|---|---|---|---|---|---|---|---|
| 0° | 1.57080 | 1.57080 | 50° | 1.93558 | 1.30554 | 82° 0′ | 3.36987 | 1.02784 |
| 1 | 092 | 068 | 51 | 5386 | 29628 | 12 | 9457 | 670 |
| 2 | 127 | 032 | 52 | 7288 | 28695 | 24 | 3.41994 | 558 |
| 3 | 187 | 1.56972 | 53 | 9267 | 27757 | 36 | 4601 | 447 |
| 4 | 271 | 888 | 54 | 2.01327 | 26815 | 48 | 7282 | 338 |
| 5 | 379 | 781 | 55 | 3472 | 25868 | 83 0 | 3.50042 | 231 |
| 6 | 511 | 650 | 56 | 5706 | 24918 | 12 | 2884 | 126 |
| 7 | 668 | 495 | 57 | 8036 | 23966 | 24 | 5814 | 023 |
| 8 | 849 | 296 | 58 | 2.10466 | 23013 | 36 | 8837 | 1921 |
| 9 | 1.58054 | 114 | 59 | 3002 | 22059 | 48 | 3.61959 | 821 |
| 10 | 284 | 1.55889 | 60 | 2.15652 | 21106 | 84 0 | 3.65186 | 1.01724 |
| 11 | 539 | 640 | 61 | 8421 | 20154 | 12 | 8525 | 628 |
| 12 | 820 | 368 | 62 | 2.21319 | 19205 | 24 | 3.71984 | 534 |
| 13 | 1.59125 | 073 | 63 | 4355 | 18259 | 36 | 5572 | 443 |
| 14 | 457 | 1.54755 | 64 | 7538 | 17318 | 48 | 9298 | 354 |
| 15 | 814 | 415 | 65 | 2.30879 | 16383 | 85 0 | 3.83174 | 266 |
| 16 | 1.60198 | 052 | 66 | 4390 | 15455 | 12 | 7211 | 181 |
| 17 | 608 | 1.53667 | 67 | 8087 | 14535 | 24 | 3.91423 | 099 |
| 18 | 1.61045 | 260 | 68 | 2.41984 | 13624 | 36 | 5827 | 018 |
| 19 | 510 | 1.52831 | 69 | 6100 | 12725 | 48 | 4.00437 | 0940 |
| 20 | 1.62003 | 380 | 70° 0′ | 2.50455 | 11838 | 86 0 | 5276 | 865 |
| 21 | 523 | 1.51908 | 30 | 2729 | 11399 | 12 | 4.10366 | 792 |
| 22 | 1.63073 | 415 | 71 0 | 5073 | 10964 | 24 | 5736 | 721 |
| 23 | 632 | 1.50901 | 30 | 7490 | 10533 | 36 | 4.21416 | 653 |
| 24 | 1.64260 | 366 | 72 0 | 9982 | 106 | 48 | 7444 | 588 |
| 25 | 900 | 1.49811 | 30 | 2.62555 | 09683 | 87 0 | 4.33865 | 526 |
| 26 | 1.65570 | 237 | 73 0 | 5214 | 265 | 12 | 40733 | 466 |
| 27 | 6272 | 1.48643 | 30 | 7962 | 8851 | 24 | 8115 | 410 |
| 28 | 7006 | 029 | 74 0 | 2.70807 | 443 | 36 | 56190 | 356 |
| 29 | 7773 | 1.47397 | 30 | 3752 | 039 | 48 | 64765 | 306 |
| 30 | 1.68575 | 1.46746 | 75 0 | 6806 | 7641 | 88 0 | 74272 | 258 |
| 31 | 9411 | 077 | 30 | 9975 | 248 | 12 | 84785 | 215 |
| 32 | 1.70284 | 1.45391 | 76 0 | 2.83267 | 6861 | 24 | 96542 | 174 |
| 33 | 1192 | 44687 | 30 | 6691 | 480 | 36 | 5.09876 | 137 |
| 34 | 2139 | 43966 | 77 0 | 2.90256 | 106 | 48 | 25274 | 104 |
| 35 | 3125 | 229 | 30 | 3974 | 5738 | 89 0 | 43491 | 075 |
| 36 | 4150 | 42476 | 78 0 | 7857 | 378 | 6 | 54020 | 062 |
| 37 | 5217 | 41707 | 30 | 3.01918 | 024 | 12 | 65792 | 050 |
| 38 | 6326 | 40924 | 79 0 | 6173 | 4679 | 18 | 79140 | 049 |
| 39 | 7479 | 126 | 30 | 3.10640 | 4341 | 24 | 94550 | 030 |
| 40 | 1.78677 | 1.39314 | 80 0 | 5339 | 011 | 30 | 6.12778 | 021 |
| 41 | 9922 | 38489 | 12 | 7288 | 3882 | 36 | 35038 | 014 |
| 42 | 1.81216 | 37650 | 24 | 9280 | 754 | 42 | 63854 | 008 |
| 43 | 2560 | 36800 | 36 | 3.21317 | 628 | 48 | 7.04398 | 004 |
| 44 | 3957 | 35938 | 48 | 3400 | 503 | 54 | 73711 | 011 |
| 45 | 5407 | 35064 | 81 0 | 5530 | 379 | 90 | ∞ | 000 |
| 46 | 6915 | 34181 | 12 | 7711 | 257 | | | |
| 47 | 8481 | 33287 | 24 | 9945 | 126 | | | |
| 48 | 1.90108 | 32384 | 36 | 3.32234 | 017 | | | |
| 49 | 1800 | 31473 | 48 | 4580 | 2900 | | | |

## II.—ELLIPTIC INTEGRALS OF THE FIRST KIND

| φ | θ | | | | | | | | | |
|---|---|---|---|---|---|---|---|---|---|---|
| | 0° | 5° | 10° | 15° | 20° | 25° | 30° | 35° | 40° | 45° |
| 1 | 0.01745 | 0.01745 | 0.01745 | 0.01745 | 0.01745 | 0.01745 | 0.01745 | 0.01745 | 0.01745 | 0.01745 |
| 2 | 03491 | 03491 | 03491 | 03491 | 03491 | 03491 | 03491 | 03491 | 03491 | 03491 |
| 3 | 05236 | 05236 | 05236 | 05236 | 05236 | 05236 | 05237 | 05237 | 05237 | 05237 |
| 4 | 06981 | 06981 | 06981 | 06982 | 06982 | 06982 | 06983 | 06983 | 06984 | 06984 |
| 5 | 08727 | 08727 | 08727 | 08727 | 08728 | 08729 | 08729 | 08730 | 08731 | 08732 |
| 6 | 10472 | 10472 | 10473 | 10473 | 10474 | 10475 | 10477 | 10478 | 10480 | 10482 |
| 7 | 12217 | 12218 | 12218 | 12219 | 12221 | 12223 | 12225 | 12227 | 12230 | 12233 |
| 8 | 13963 | 13963 | 13964 | 13966 | 13968 | 13971 | 13974 | 13978 | 13981 | 13985 |
| 9 | 15708 | 15708 | 15710 | 15712 | 15715 | 15719 | 15724 | 15729 | 15735 | 15740 |
| 10 | 17453 | 17454 | 17456 | 17459 | 17464 | 17469 | 17475 | 17482 | 17490 | 17498 |
| 11 | 19199 | 19200 | 19202 | 19206 | 19212 | 19220 | 19228 | 19237 | 19247 | 19258 |
| 12 | 20944 | 20945 | 20949 | 20954 | 20962 | 20971 | 20982 | 20994 | 21007 | 21021 |
| 13 | 22689 | 22691 | 22695 | 22702 | 22712 | 22724 | 22738 | 22753 | 22770 | 22787 |
| 14 | 24435 | 24436 | 24442 | 24451 | 24463 | 24478 | 24495 | 24514 | 24535 | 24556 |
| 15 | 26180 | 26182 | 26189 | 26200 | 26215 | 26233 | 26254 | 26278 | 26303 | 26330 |
| 16 | 27925 | 27928 | 27936 | 27949 | 27967 | 27989 | 28015 | 28044 | 28075 | 28107 |
| 17 | 29671 | 29674 | 29684 | 29699 | 29721 | 29748 | 29779 | 29813 | 29850 | 29889 |
| 18 | 31416 | 31420 | 31431 | 31450 | 31475 | 31507 | 31544 | 31585 | 31629 | 31675 |
| 19 | 33161 | 33166 | 33179 | 33201 | 33231 | 33268 | 33312 | 33360 | 33412 | 33466 |
| 20 | 34907 | 34912 | 34927 | 34953 | 34988 | 35031 | 35082 | 35138 | 35199 | 35262 |
| 21 | 36652 | 36658 | 36676 | 36706 | 36746 | 36796 | 36855 | 36920 | 36990 | 37063 |
| 22 | 38397 | 38404 | 38425 | 38459 | 38505 | 38563 | 38630 | 38705 | 38786 | 38871 |
| 23 | 40143 | 40151 | 40174 | 40213 | 40266 | 40331 | 40408 | 40494 | 40587 | 40683 |
| 24 | 41888 | 41897 | 41924 | 41968 | 42027 | 42102 | 42189 | 42287 | 42392 | 42503 |
| 25 | 43633 | 43643 | 43674 | 43723 | 43791 | 43875 | 43973 | 44084 | 44203 | 44328 |
| 26 | 45379 | 45390 | 45424 | 45479 | 45555 | 45650 | 45761 | 45885 | 46020 | 46161 |
| 27 | 47124 | 47141 | 47174 | 47236 | 47321 | 47427 | 47551 | 47690 | 47841 | 48000 |
| 28 | 48869 | 48883 | 48925 | 48994 | 49089 | 49207 | 49345 | 49500 | 49669 | 49846 |
| 29 | 50615 | 50630 | 50677 | 50753 | 50858 | 50988 | 51142 | 51315 | 51503 | 51700 |
| 30 | 52360 | 52377 | 52428 | 52513 | 52628 | 52773 | 52943 | 53134 | 53343 | 53562 |
| 31 | 54105 | 54124 | 54181 | 54273 | 54401 | 54560 | 54747 | 54959 | 55189 | 55432 |
| 32 | 55851 | 55871 | 55933 | 56035 | 56175 | 56349 | 56555 | 56788 | 57042 | 57310 |
| 33 | 57596 | 57619 | 57686 | 57797 | 57950 | 58141 | 58367 | 58623 | 58902 | 59197 |
| 34 | 59341 | 59366 | 59439 | 59561 | 59727 | 59936 | 60183 | 60463 | 60769 | 61093 |
| 35 | 61087 | 61113 | 61193 | 61325 | 61506 | 61734 | 62003 | 62308 | 62643 | 62998 |
| 36 | 62832 | 62861 | 62948 | 63090 | 63287 | 63534 | 63827 | 64159 | 64524 | 64912 |
| 37 | 64577 | 64609 | 64702 | 64857 | 65070 | 65337 | 65655 | 66016 | 66413 | 66836 |
| 38 | 66323 | 66356 | 66457 | 66624 | 66854 | 67144 | 67487 | 67879 | 68309 | 68769 |
| 39 | 68068 | 68104 | 68213 | 68393 | 68641 | 68953 | 69324 | 69747 | 70214 | 70713 |
| 40 | 69813 | 69852 | 69969 | 70162 | 70429 | 70765 | 71165 | 71622 | 72126 | 72667 |
| 41 | 71558 | 71600 | 71726 | 71933 | 72219 | 72580 | 73010 | 73502 | 74047 | 74632 |
| 42 | 73304 | 73349 | 73483 | 73704 | 74011 | 74398 | 74860 | 75389 | 75976 | 76608 |
| 43 | 75049 | 75097 | 75240 | 75477 | 75805 | 76219 | 76714 | 77282 | 77914 | 78594 |
| 44 | 76794 | 76846 | 76998 | 77251 | 77600 | 78043 | 78573 | 79182 | 79860 | 80592 |
| 45 | 0.78540 | 0.78594 | 0.78756 | 0.79025 | 0.79398 | 0.79871 | 0.80437 | 0.81088 | 0.81815 | 0.82602 |

## II.—ELLIPTIC INTEGRALS OF THE FIRST KIND

| φ | θ | | | | | | | | |
|---|---|---|---|---|---|---|---|---|---|
| | 50° | 55° | 60° | 65° | 70° | 75° | 80° | 85° | 90° |
| 1 | 0.01745 | 0.01745 | 0.01745 | 0.01745 | 0.01745 | 0.01745 | 0.01745 | 0.01745 | 0.01745 |
| 2 | 03491 | 03491 | 03491 | 03491 | 03491 | 03491 | 03491 | 03491 | 03491 |
| 3 | 05237 | 05238 | 05238 | 05238 | 05238 | 05238 | 05238 | 05238 | 05238 |
| 4 | 06985 | 06985 | 06986 | 06986 | 06986 | 06987 | 06987 | 06987 | 06987 |
| 5 | 08733 | 08734 | 08735 | 08736 | 08736 | 08737 | 08737 | 08738 | 08738 |
| 6 | 10483 | 10485 | 10486 | 10488 | 10489 | 10490 | 10491 | 10491 | 10491 |
| 7 | 12235 | 12238 | 12240 | 12242 | 12244 | 12246 | 12247 | 12248 | 12248 |
| 8 | 13989 | 13993 | 13997 | 14000 | 14003 | 14005 | 14007 | 14008 | 14008 |
| 9 | 15746 | 15751 | 15757 | 15761 | 15765 | 15769 | 15771 | 15772 | 15773 |
| 10 | 17505 | 17513 | 17520 | 17526 | 17532 | 17536 | 17540 | 17542 | 17543 |
| 11 | 19268 | 19278 | 19288 | 19296 | 19304 | 19310 | 19314 | 19317 | 19318 |
| 12 | 21034 | 21047 | 21059 | 21071 | 21080 | 21088 | 21094 | 21098 | 21099 |
| 13 | 22804 | 22821 | 22836 | 22851 | 22863 | 22873 | 22880 | 22885 | 22886 |
| 14 | 24578 | 24599 | 24618 | 24636 | 24652 | 24664 | 24674 | 24680 | 24681 |
| 15 | 26356 | 26382 | 26406 | 26428 | 26448 | 26463 | 26475 | 26482 | 26484 |
| 16 | 28139 | 28171 | 28200 | 28227 | 28251 | 28270 | 28284 | 28293 | 28295 |
| 17 | 29927 | 29965 | 30001 | 30034 | 30062 | 30085 | 30102 | 30112 | 30116 |
| 18 | 31721 | 31766 | 31809 | 31848 | 31881 | 31909 | 31929 | 31942 | 31946 |
| 19 | 33520 | 33574 | 33624 | 33670 | 33710 | 33742 | 33766 | 33781 | 33786 |
| 20 | 35326 | 35388 | 35447 | 35501 | 35548 | 35586 | 35615 | 35632 | 35638 |
| 21 | 37137 | 37210 | 37279 | 37342 | 37396 | 37441 | 37474 | 37494 | 37501 |
| 22 | 38956 | 39040 | 39119 | 39192 | 39255 | 39307 | 39346 | 39369 | 39377 |
| 23 | 40782 | 40878 | 40969 | 41053 | 41126 | 41186 | 41230 | 41257 | 41266 |
| 24 | 42614 | 42724 | 42829 | 42925 | 43008 | 43077 | 43128 | 43159 | 43169 |
| 25 | 44455 | 44580 | 44699 | 44808 | 44904 | 44982 | 45040 | 45075 | 45088 |
| 26 | 46304 | 46445 | 46580 | 46704 | 46812 | 46901 | 46967 | 47008 | 47021 |
| 27 | 48161 | 48320 | 48472 | 48612 | 48735 | 48835 | 48910 | 48956 | 48972 |
| 28 | 50027 | 50206 | 50377 | 50534 | 50672 | 50785 | 50870 | 50922 | 50939 |
| 29 | 51902 | 52102 | 52293 | 52470 | 52624 | 52752 | 52847 | 52905 | 52925 |
| 30 | 53787 | 54009 | 54223 | 54420 | 54593 | 54736 | 54843 | 54908 | 54931 |
| 31 | 55681 | 55928 | 56166 | 56386 | 56579 | 56739 | 56858 | 56931 | 55956 |
| 32 | 57586 | 57860 | 58123 | 58367 | 58582 | 58760 | 58893 | 58975 | 59003 |
| 33 | 59501 | 59803 | 60095 | 60365 | 60604 | 60802 | 60950 | 61042 | 61073 |
| 34 | 61427 | 61760 | 62082 | 62381 | 62646 | 62865 | 63029 | 63131 | 63166 |
| 35 | 63364 | 63730 | 64085 | 64415 | 64707 | 64950 | 65132 | 65245 | 65284 |
| 36 | 65313 | 65715 | 66104 | 66468 | 66790 | 67058 | 67260 | 67385 | 67428 |
| 37 | 67273 | 67713 | 68141 | 68540 | 68895 | 69131 | 69414 | 69552 | 69599 |
| 38 | 69246 | 69727 | 70195 | 70633 | 71023 | 71349 | 71594 | 71747 | 71799 |
| 39 | 71232 | 71756 | 72267 | 72746 | 73175 | 73533 | 73804 | 73972 | 74029 |
| 40 | 73231 | 73801 | 74358 | 74882 | 75352 | 75745 | 76043 | 76228 | 76291 |
| 41 | 75243 | 75862 | 76469 | 77041 | 77555 | 77987 | 78313 | 78517 | 78586 |
| 42 | 77269 | 77940 | 78600 | 79224 | 79786 | 80258 | 80617 | 80841 | 80917 |
| 43 | 79308 | 80035 | 80752 | 81432 | 82045 | 82562 | 82954 | 83200 | 83284 |
| 44 | 81362 | 82149 | 82926 | 83665 | 84333 | 84898 | 85329 | 85598 | 85690 |
| 45 | 0.83431 | 0.84281 | 0.85122 | 0.85925 | 0.86653 | 0.87270 | 0.87741 | 0.88037 | 0.88137 |

## II.—ELLIPTIC INTEGRALS OF THE FIRST KIND

| φ | θ | | | | | | | | | |
|---|---|---|---|---|---|---|---|---|---|---|
| | 0° | 5° | 10° | 15° | 20° | 25° | 30° | 35° | 40° | 45° |
| 46° | 0.80285 | 0.80343 | 0.80515 | 0.80801 | 0.81198 | 0.81701 | 0.82305 | 0.83001 | 0.83779 | 0.84623 |
| 47 | 82030 | 82092 | 82275 | 82578 | 82999 | 83535 | 84178 | 84920 | 85752 | 86656 |
| 48 | 83776 | 83841 | 84035 | 84356 | 84803 | 85371 | 86055 | 86846 | 87734 | 88701 |
| 49 | 85521 | 85590 | 85795 | 86135 | 86609 | 87211 | 87937 | 88779 | 89725 | 90759 |
| 50 | 87266 | 87339 | 87556 | 87915 | 88416 | 89054 | 89825 | 90719 | 91725 | 92829 |
| 51 | 89012 | 89088 | 89317 | 89697 | 90226 | 90901 | 91716 | 92665 | 93735 | 94912 |
| 52 | 90757 | 90838 | 91078 | 91479 | 92037 | 92750 | 93613 | 94618 | 95755 | 97007 |
| 53 | 92502 | 92587 | 92841 | 93262 | 93850 | 94603 | 95514 | 96578 | 97784 | 0.99115 |
| 54 | 94248 | 94337 | 94603 | 95047 | 95666 | 96458 | 97420 | 0.98545 | 0.99822 | 1.01237 |
| 55 | 95993 | 96086 | 96366 | 96832 | 97483 | 0.98317 | 0.99331 | 1.00519 | 1.01871 | 03371 |
| 56 | 97738 | 97836 | 98130 | 0.98618 | 0.99302 | 1.00179 | 1.01247 | 02499 | 03928 | 05519 |
| 57 | 0.99484 | 0.99586 | 0.99894 | 1.00406 | 1.01123 | 02044 | 03167 | 04487 | 05996 | 07680 |
| 58 | 1.01229 | 1.01336 | 1.01658 | 02194 | 02946 | 03912 | 05092 | 06481 | 08073 | 09854 |
| 59 | 02974 | 03086 | 03423 | 03984 | 04770 | 05783 | 07021 | 08482 | 10159 | 12042 |
| 60 | 04720 | 04837 | 05188 | 05774 | 06597 | 07657 | 08955 | 10490 | 12256 | 14243 |
| 61 | 06465 | 06587 | 06954 | 07566 | 08425 | 09534 | 10894 | 12504 | 14361 | 16457 |
| 62 | 08210 | 08338 | 08720 | 09358 | 10255 | 11414 | 12837 | 14525 | 16476 | 18685 |
| 63 | 09956 | 10088 | 10486 | 11151 | 12087 | 13296 | 14784 | 16552 | 18601 | 20926 |
| 64 | 11701 | 11839 | 12253 | 12945 | 13920 | 15182 | 16735 | 18586 | 20735 | 23180 |
| 65 | 13446 | 13590 | 14020 | 14740 | 15755 | 17070 | 18691 | 20626 | 22877 | 25447 |
| 66 | 15192 | 15340 | 15787 | 16536 | 17592 | 18961 | 20651 | 22672 | 25029 | 27727 |
| 67 | 16937 | 17091 | 17555 | 18333 | 19430 | 20854 | 22615 | 24724 | 27190 | 30020 |
| 68 | 18682 | 18842 | 19324 | 20130 | 21269 | 22750 | 24583 | 26782 | 29359 | 32325 |
| 69 | 20428 | 20593 | 21092 | 21928 | 23110 | 24648 | 26555 | 28846 | 31537 | 34642 |
| 70 | 22173 | 22345 | 22861 | 23727 | 24953 | 26548 | 28530 | 30915 | 33723 | 36972 |
| 71 | 23918 | 24096 | 24630 | 25527 | 26796 | 28451 | 30509 | 32990 | 35917 | 39313 |
| 72 | 25664 | 25847 | 26400 | 27328 | 28641 | 30356 | 32491 | 35070 | 38118 | 41666 |
| 73 | 27409 | 27599 | 28169 | 29129 | 30488 | 32263 | 34477 | 37155 | 40328 | 44030 |
| 74 | 29154 | 29350 | 29939 | 30930 | 32335 | 34172 | 36466 | 39244 | 42544 | 46404 |
| 75 | 30900 | 31102 | 31710 | 32733 | 34184 | 36083 | 38457 | 41339 | 44767 | 48788 |
| 76 | 32645 | 32853 | 33480 | 34535 | 36034 | 37996 | 40452 | 43437 | 46997 | 51183 |
| 77 | 34390 | 34605 | 35251 | 36339 | 37884 | 39911 | 42449 | 45540 | 49232 | 53586 |
| 78 | 36136 | 36356 | 37022 | 38143 | 39736 | 41827 | 44449 | 47647 | 51474 | 55999 |
| 79 | 37881 | 38108 | 38793 | 39947 | 41588 | 43744 | 46451 | 49757 | 53721 | 58419 |
| 80 | 39626 | 39860 | 40565 | 41752 | 43442 | 45663 | 48455 | 51870 | 55973 | 60848 |
| 81 | 41372 | 41612 | 42336 | 43557 | 45296 | 47583 | 50462 | 53987 | 58230 | 63283 |
| 82 | 43117 | 43364 | 44108 | 45362 | 47150 | 49504 | 52470 | 56106 | 60491 | 65725 |
| 83 | 44862 | 45115 | 45879 | 47168 | 49005 | 51426 | 54479 | 58228 | 62756 | 68172 |
| 84 | 46608 | 46867 | 47651 | 48974 | 50861 | 53350 | 56490 | 60352 | 65024 | 70625 |
| 85 | 48353 | 48619 | 49423 | 50781 | 52717 | 55273 | 58503 | 62478 | 67295 | 73082 |
| 86 | 50098 | 50371 | 51195 | 52587 | 54574 | 57198 | 60516 | 64605 | 69569 | 75542 |
| 87 | 51844 | 52123 | 52968 | 54394 | 56431 | 59123 | 62530 | 66734 | 71844 | 78006 |
| 88 | 53589 | 53875 | 54740 | 56200 | 58288 | 61048 | 64545 | 68864 | 74121 | 80472 |
| 89 | 55334 | 55627 | 56512 | 58007 | 60145 | 62974 | 66560 | 70994 | 76399 | 82939 |
| 90 | 1.57080 | 1.57379 | 1.58284 | 1.59814 | 1.62003 | 1.64900 | 1,68575 | 1.73125 | 1.78677 | 1.85407 |

## II.—ELLIPTIC INTEGRALS OF THE FIRST KIND

| φ | θ | | | | | | | | |
|---|---|---|---|---|---|---|---|---|---|
| | 50° | 55° | 60° | 65° | 70° | 75° | 80° | 85° | 90° |
| 46° | 0.85515 | 0.86431 | 0.87342 | 0.88213 | 0.89005 | 0.89678 | 0.90193 | 0.90517 | 0.90628 |
| 47 | 87614 | 88601 | 89585 | 90529 | 91390 | 92224 | 92687 | 93042 | 93163 |
| 48 | 89729 | 90791 | 91853 | 92875 | 93811 | 94610 | 95226 | 95614 | 95747 |
| 49 | 91860 | 93001 | 94146 | 95252 | 96267 | 97139 | 0.97810 | 0.98235 | 0.98381 |
| 50 | 94008 | 95232 | 96465 | 0.97660 | 0.98762 | 0.99711 | 1.00444 | 1.00909 | 1.01068 |
| 51 | 96171 | 97484 | 0.98811 | 1.00102 | 1.01297 | 1.02329 | 03129 | 03638 | 03812 |
| 52 | 0.98352 | 0.99759 | 1.01185 | 02578 | 03872 | 04995 | 05868 | 06425 | 06616 |
| 53 | 1.00550 | 1.02055 | 03587 | 05089 | 06491 | 07711 | 08665 | 09274 | 09483 |
| 54 | 02765 | 04374 | 06018 | 07637 | 09155 | 10481 | 11521 | 12188 | 12418 |
| 55 | 04998 | 06716 | 08479 | 10223 | 11865 | 13307 | 14442 | 15171 | 15423 |
| 56 | 07248 | 09082 | 10971 | 12848 | 14624 | 16190 | 17430 | 18229 | 18505 |
| 57 | 09517 | 11472 | 13494 | 15513 | 17433 | 19136 | 20488 | 21364 | 21667 |
| 58 | 11803 | 13886 | 16050 | 18220 | 20295 | 22145 | 23623 | 24582 | 24916 |
| 59 | 14108 | 16325 | 18638 | 20970 | 23212 | 25223 | 26837 | 27890 | 28257 |
| 60 | 16432 | 18788 | 21254 | 23764 | 26186 | 28371 | 30135 | 31292 | 31696 |
| 61 | 18773 | 21277 | 23916 | 26604 | 29219 | 31594 | 33524 | 34795 | 35240 |
| 62 | 21134 | 23792 | 26606 | 29490 | 32314 | 34897 | 37008 | 38407 | 38899 |
| 63 | 23513 | 26332 | 29332 | 32425 | 35473 | 38281 | 40594 | 42135 | 42679 |
| 64 | 25910 | 28898 | 32094 | 35409 | 38699 | 41753 | 44288 | 45989 | 46591 |
| 65 | 28326 | 31491 | 34893 | 38443 | 41994 | 45316 | 48098 | 49977 | 50645 |
| 66 | 30760 | 34109 | 37728 | 41529 | 45360 | 48976 | 52031 | 54112 | 54855 |
| 67 | 33212 | 36753 | 40600 | 44668 | 48800 | 52738 | 56096 | 58404 | 59232 |
| 68 | 35683 | 39423 | 43510 | 47860 | 52317 | 56606 | 60303 | 62868 | 63794 |
| 69 | 38171 | 42119 | 46457 | 51107 | 55913 | 60586 | 64661 | 67518 | 68557 |
| 70 | 40677 | 44840 | 49441 | 54410 | 59591 | 64684 | 69181 | 72372 | 73542 |
| 71 | 43200 | 47587 | 52463 | 57768 | 63352 | 68905 | 73877 | 77450 | 78771 |
| 72 | 45739 | 50359 | 55522 | 61182 | 67198 | 73256 | 78759 | 82774 | 84273 |
| 73 | 48296 | 53155 | 58618 | 64653 | 71132 | 77743 | 83844 | 88370 | 90079 |
| 74 | 50867 | 55974 | 61750 | 68180 | 75155 | 82371 | 89146 | 1.94267 | 1.96226 |
| 75 | 53455 | 58817 | 64918 | 71763 | 79269 | 87145 | 1.94682 | 2.00499 | 2.02759 |
| 76 | 56056 | 61682 | 68120 | 75401 | 83473 | 92073 | 2.00470 | 07106 | 09732 |
| 77 | 58672 | 64569 | 71356 | 79094 | 87768 | 1.97157 | 06529 | 14136 | 17212 |
| 78 | 61302 | 67476 | 74625 | 82840 | 92154 | 2.02403 | 12878 | 21644 | 25280 |
| 79 | 63943 | 70403 | 77924 | 86637 | 1.96630 | 07813 | 19538 | 29694 | 34040 |
| 80 | 66597 | 73347 | 81253 | 90484 | 2.01193 | 13390 | 26527 | 38365 | 43625 |
| 81 | 69261 | 76309 | 84609 | 94377 | 05840 | 19131 | 33866 | 47748 | 54209 |
| 82 | 71935 | 79286 | 87991 | 1.98313 | 10568 | 25035 | 41569 | 57954 | 66031 |
| 83 | 74618 | 82278 | 91395 | 2.02290 | 15371 | 31097 | 49648 | 69109 | 79422 |
| 84 | 77309 | 85281 | 94821 | 06303 | 20244 | 37309 | 58105 | 81362 | 2.94870 |
| 85 | 80006 | 88296 | 1.98264 | 10348 | 25178 | 43658 | 66935 | 2.94869 | 3.13130 |
| 86 | 82710 | 91320 | 2.01723 | 14421 | 30166 | 50129 | 76116 | 3.09782 | 35467 |
| 87 | 85418 | 94351 | 05194 | 18515 | 35198 | 56703 | 85612 | 26198 | 3.64253 |
| 88 | 88129 | 1.97388 | 08674 | 22627 | 40265 | 63357 | 2.95366 | 44116 | 4.04813 |
| 89 | 90843 | 2.00429 | 12161 | 26750 | 45354 | 70068 | 3.05304 | 63279 | 4.74135 |
| 90 | 1.93558 | 2.03472 | 2.15652 | 2.30879 | 2.50455 | 2.76806 | 3.15339 | 3.83174 | ∞ |

## III.—ELLIPTIC INTEGRALS OF THE SECOND KIND

| φ | θ | | | | | | | | | |
|---|---|---|---|---|---|---|---|---|---|---|
| | 0° | 5° | 10° | 15° | 20° | 25° | 30° | 35° | 40° | 45° |
| 1 | 0.01745 | 0.01745 | 0.01745 | 0.01745 | 0.01745 | 0.01745 | 0.01745 | 0.01745 | 0.01745 | 0.01745 |
| 2 | 03491 | 03491 | 03491 | 03491 | 03491 | 03491 | 03490 | 03490 | 03490 | 03490 |
| 3 | 05236 | 05236 | 05236 | 05236 | 05236 | 05236 | 05235 | 05235 | 05235 | 05235 |
| 4 | 06981 | 06981 | 06981 | 06981 | 06981 | 06980 | 06980 | 06979 | 06979 | 06978 |
| 5 | 08727 | 08727 | 08726 | 08726 | 08725 | 08725 | 08744 | 08723 | 08722 | 08721 |
| 6 | 10472 | 10472 | 10471 | 10471 | 10470 | 10469 | 10467 | 10466 | 10464 | 10462 |
| 7 | 12217 | 12217 | 12216 | 12215 | 12214 | 12212 | 12210 | 12207 | 12205 | 12202 |
| 8 | 13963 | 13962 | 13961 | 13960 | 13957 | 13955 | 13951 | 13948 | 13944 | 13940 |
| 9 | 15708 | 15707 | 15706 | 15704 | 15700 | 15696 | 15692 | 15687 | 15681 | 15676 |
| 10 | 17453 | 17453 | 17451 | 17447 | 17443 | 17438 | 17431 | 17427 | 17417 | 17409 |
| 11 | 19199 | 19198 | 19195 | 19191 | 19185 | 19178 | 19169 | 19160 | 19150 | 19140 |
| 12 | 20944 | 20943 | 20939 | 20934 | 20926 | 20917 | 20906 | 20894 | 20881 | 20868 |
| 13 | 22689 | 22688 | 22683 | 22676 | 22667 | 22655 | 22641 | 22626 | 22609 | 22593 |
| 14 | 24435 | 24433 | 24427 | 24419 | 24406 | 24392 | 24374 | 24355 | 24335 | 24314 |
| 15 | 26180 | 26178 | 26171 | 26160 | 26145 | 26127 | 26106 | 26083 | 26058 | 26032 |
| 16 | 27925 | 27923 | 27914 | 27901 | 27883 | 27861 | 27836 | 27807 | 27777 | 27746 |
| 17 | 29671 | 29667 | 29658 | 29642 | 29620 | 29594 | 29563 | 29529 | 29493 | 29455 |
| 18 | 31416 | 31412 | 31401 | 31382 | 31357 | 31325 | 31289 | 31248 | 31205 | 31161 |
| 19 | 33161 | 33157 | 33143 | 33121 | 33092 | 33055 | 33012 | 32965 | 32914 | 32862 |
| 20 | 34907 | 34901 | 34886 | 34860 | 34825 | 34783 | 34733 | 34678 | 34619 | 34558 |
| 21 | 36652 | 36646 | 36628 | 36598 | 36558 | 36509 | 36451 | 36387 | 36319 | 36249 |
| 22 | 38397 | 38390 | 38370 | 38336 | 38290 | 38233 | 38167 | 38094 | 38015 | 37934 |
| 23 | 40143 | 40135 | 40111 | 40073 | 40020 | 39955 | 39880 | 39796 | 39707 | 39614 |
| 24 | 41888 | 41879 | 41852 | 41819 | 41749 | 41676 | 41590 | 41496 | 41394 | 41289 |
| 25 | 43633 | 43623 | 43593 | 43544 | 43477 | 43394 | 43298 | 43191 | 43076 | 42958 |
| 26 | 45379 | 45367 | 45333 | 45278 | 45203 | 45110 | 45002 | 44882 | 44753 | 44620 |
| 27 | 47124 | 47111 | 47074 | 47012 | 46928 | 46824 | 46703 | 46569 | 46425 | 46276 |
| 28 | 48869 | 48855 | 48813 | 48745 | 48651 | 48536 | 48402 | 48252 | 48092 | 47926 |
| 29 | 50615 | 50599 | 50553 | 50477 | 50373 | 50245 | 50097 | 49931 | 49753 | 49569 |
| 30 | 52360 | 52343 | 52292 | 52208 | 52094 | 51953 | 51788 | 51605 | 51409 | 51205 |
| 31 | 54105 | 54086 | 54030 | 53938 | 53813 | 53657 | 53476 | 53275 | 53059 | 52834 |
| 32 | 55851 | 55830 | 55768 | 55667 | 55530 | 55360 | 55161 | 54940 | 54703 | 54456 |
| 33 | 57596 | 57573 | 57506 | 57396 | 57245 | 57059 | 56842 | 56600 | 56341 | 56070 |
| 34 | 59341 | 59317 | 59243 | 59123 | 58959 | 58756 | 58520 | 58256 | 57972 | 57677 |
| 35 | 61087 | 61060 | 60980 | 60850 | 60672 | 60451 | 60194 | 59907 | 59598 | 59276 |
| 36 | 62832 | 62803 | 62716 | 62575 | 62382 | 62143 | 61864 | 61552 | 61217 | 60868 |
| 37 | 64577 | 64546 | 64452 | 64300 | 64091 | 63832 | 63530 | 63193 | 62830 | 62451 |
| 38 | 66323 | 66289 | 66188 | 66023 | 65798 | 65519 | 65193 | 64828 | 64436 | 64027 |
| 39 | 68068 | 68031 | 67923 | 67746 | 67503 | 67203 | 66851 | 66459 | 66035 | 65594 |
| 40 | 69813 | 69774 | 69658 | 69467 | 69207 | 68884 | 68506 | 68084 | 67628 | 67153 |
| 41 | 71558 | 71517 | 71392 | 71188 | 70909 | 70562 | 70157 | 69703 | 69214 | 68703 |
| 42 | 73304 | 73259 | 73126 | 72907 | 72609 | 72238 | 71804 | 71318 | 70793 | 70245 |
| 43 | 75049 | 75001 | 74859 | 74626 | 74307 | 73910 | 73446 | 72927 | 72365 | 71778 |
| 44 | 76794 | 76744 | 76592 | 76343 | 76003 | 75580 | 75085 | 74530 | 73931 | 73303 |
| 45 | 0.78540 | 0.78486 | 0.78324 | 0.78059 | 0.77697 | 0.77247 | 0.76720 | 0.76128 | 0.75489 | 0.74819 |

## III.—ELLIPTIC INTEGRALS OF THE SECOND KIND

| φ | θ | | | | | | | | |
|---|---|---|---|---|---|---|---|---|---|
| | 50° | 55° | 60° | 65° | 70° | 75° | 80° | 85° | 90° |
| 1° | 0.01745 | 0.01745 | 0.01745 | 0.01745 | 0.01745 | 0.01745 | 0.01745 | 0.01745 | 0.01745 |
| 2 | 03490 | 03490 | 03490 | 03490 | 03490 | 03490 | 03490 | 03490 | 03490 |
| 3 | 05235 | 05234 | 05234 | 05234 | 05234 | 05234 | 05234 | 05234 | 05234 |
| 4 | 06978 | 06978 | 06977 | 06977 | 06976 | 06976 | 06976 | 06976 | 06976 |
| 5 | 08720 | 08719 | 08718 | 08718 | 08717 | 08716 | 08716 | 08716 | 08716 |
| 6 | 10461 | 10459 | 10458 | 10456 | 10455 | 10454 | 10453 | 10453 | 10453 |
| 7 | 12199 | 12197 | 12195 | 12192 | 12190 | 12189 | 12188 | 12187 | 12187 |
| 8 | 13936 | 13932 | 13929 | 13925 | 13923 | 13920 | 13919 | 13918 | 13917 |
| 9 | 15670 | 15665 | 15660 | 15655 | 15651 | 15648 | 15645 | 15644 | 15643 |
| 10 | 17401 | 17394 | 17387 | 17381 | 17375 | 17371 | 17367 | 17365 | 17365 |
| 11 | 19130 | 19120 | 19110 | 19102 | 19095 | 19089 | 19084 | 19082 | 19081 |
| 12 | 20855 | 20842 | 20830 | 20819 | 20809 | 20801 | 20796 | 20792 | 20791 |
| 13 | 22576 | 22559 | 22544 | 22530 | 22518 | 22508 | 22501 | 22497 | 22495 |
| 14 | 24293 | 24272 | 24253 | 24236 | 24221 | 24209 | 24200 | 24194 | 24192 |
| 15 | 26006 | 25981 | 25957 | 25936 | 25917 | 25902 | 25891 | 25884 | 25882 |
| 16 | 27714 | 27684 | 27655 | 27629 | 27606 | 27588 | 27575 | 27567 | 27564 |
| 17 | 29418 | 29381 | 29347 | 29315 | 29288 | 29267 | 29250 | 29241 | 29237 |
| 18 | 31116 | 31073 | 31032 | 30995 | 30963 | 30937 | 30917 | 30906 | 30902 |
| 19 | 32809 | 32758 | 32710 | 32666 | 32629 | 32598 | 32575 | 32561 | 32557 |
| 20 | 34496 | 34437 | 34381 | 34330 | 34286 | 34250 | 34224 | 34207 | 34202 |
| 21 | 36178 | 36109 | 36044 | 35985 | 35934 | 35892 | 35862 | 35843 | 35837 |
| 22 | 37853 | 37773 | 37699 | 37631 | 37572 | 37525 | 37490 | 37468 | 37461 |
| 23 | 39521 | 39431 | 39345 | 39268 | 39201 | 39146 | 39106 | 39081 | 39073 |
| 24 | 41183 | 41080 | 40983 | 40895 | 40819 | 40757 | 40711 | 40683 | 40674 |
| 25 | 42838 | 42722 | 42612 | 42513 | 42426 | 42356 | 42304 | 42273 | 42262 |
| 26 | 44486 | 44355 | 44232 | 44120 | 44023 | 43944 | 43885 | 43849 | 43837 |
| 27 | 46126 | 45980 | 45842 | 45716 | 45607 | 45518 | 45453 | 45413 | 45399 |
| 28 | 47759 | 47595 | 47441 | 47301 | 47180 | 47081 | 47007 | 46962 | 46947 |
| 29 | 49383 | 49202 | 49031 | 48875 | 48740 | 48629 | 48548 | 48498 | 48481 |
| 30 | 51000 | 50799 | 50609 | 50437 | 50287 | 50165 | 50074 | 50019 | 50000 |
| 31 | 52608 | 52386 | 52177 | 51986 | 51821 | 51686 | 51586 | 51525 | 51504 |
| 32 | 54207 | 53964 | 53733 | 53524 | 53341 | 53193 | 53082 | 53015 | 52992 |
| 33 | 55798 | 55531 | 55278 | 55048 | 54848 | 54684 | 54563 | 54489 | 54464 |
| 34 | 57379 | 57087 | 56811 | 56559 | 56340 | 56161 | 56028 | 55947 | 55919 |
| 35 | 58952 | 58634 | 58332 | 58057 | 57818 | 57622 | 57477 | 57388 | 57358 |
| 36 | 60515 | 60169 | 59841 | 59541 | 59280 | 59067 | 58909 | 58811 | 58779 |
| 37 | 62068 | 61693 | 61337 | 61011 | 60727 | 60495 | 60323 | 60217 | 60182 |
| 38 | 63612 | 63206 | 62820 | 62467 | 62159 | 61907 | 61720 | 61605 | 61566 |
| 39 | 65146 | 64707 | 64290 | 63908 | 63574 | 63302 | 63099 | 62974 | 62932 |
| 40 | 66671 | 66197 | 65746 | 65334 | 64974 | 64679 | 64459 | 64324 | 64279 |
| 41 | 68185 | 67675 | 67189 | 66745 | 66356 | 66038 | 65801 | 65655 | 65606 |
| 42 | 69688 | 69140 | 68619 | 68140 | 67722 | 67379 | 67124 | 66966 | 66913 |
| 43 | 71182 | 70594 | 70034 | 69520 | 69070 | 68701 | 68426 | 68257 | 68200 |
| 44 | 72665 | 72036 | 71435 | 70884 | 70401 | 70005 | 69710 | 69527 | 69466 |
| 45 | 0.74137 | 0.73465 | 0.72822 | 0.72232 | 0.71715 | 0.71289 | 0.70972 | 0.70777 | 0.70711 |

### III.—ELLIPTIC INTEGRALS OF THE SECOND KIND

| φ | θ | | | | | | | | | |
|---|---|---|---|---|---|---|---|---|---|---|
| | 0° | 5° | 10° | 15° | 20° | 25° | 30° | 35° | 40° | 45° |
| 46° | 0.80285 | 0.80228 | 0.80056 | 0.79775 | 0.79390 | 0.78911 | 0.78350 | 0.77721 | 0.77040 | 0.76326 |
| 47 | 82030 | 81969 | 81787 | 81489 | 81081 | 80573 | 79977 | 79308 | 78584 | 77824 |
| 48 | 83776 | 83711 | 83518 | 83202 | 82770 | 82231 | 81599 | 80890 | 80121 | 79313 |
| 49 | 85521 | 85453 | 85249 | 84914 | 84457 | 83887 | 83217 | 82466 | 81651 | 80794 |
| 50 | 87266 | 87194 | 86979 | 86626 | 86142 | 85539 | 84832 | 84036 | 83173 | 82265 |
| 51 | 89012 | 88936 | 88709 | 88336 | 87826 | 87189 | 86442 | 85601 | 84689 | 83728 |
| 52 | 90757 | 90677 | 90438 | 90045 | 89507 | 88836 | 88048 | 87161 | 86197 | 85182 |
| 53 | 92502 | 92418 | 92166 | 91753 | 91187 | 90481 | 89650 | 88715 | 87698 | 86627 |
| 54 | 94248 | 94159 | 93895 | 93450 | 92865 | 92122 | 91248 | 90264 | 89193 | 88063 |
| 55 | 95993 | 95900 | 95622 | 95166 | 94541 | 93761 | 92843 | 91807 | 90680 | 89490 |
| 56 | 97738 | 97641 | 97350 | 96872 | 96216 | 95397 | 94433 | 93345 | 92160 | 90908 |
| 57 | 0.99484 | 0.99381 | 0.99077 | 0.98576 | 97889 | 97030 | 96019 | 94878 | 93634 | 92318 |
| 58 | 1.01229 | 1.01122 | 1.00803 | 1.00279 | 0.99560 | 0.98661 | 97602 | 96405 | 95100 | 93719 |
| 59 | 02974 | 02863 | 02529 | 01981 | 1.01229 | 1.00289 | 0.99180 | 97928 | 96560 | 95111 |
| 60 | 04720 | 04603 | 04255 | 03683 | 02897 | 01915 | 1.00756 | 0.99445 | 98013 | 96495 |
| 61 | 06465 | 06343 | 05980 | 05383 | 04563 | 03538 | 02327 | 1.00957 | 0.99460 | 97871 |
| 62 | 08210 | 08084 | 07705 | 07083 | 06228 | 05158 | 03895 | 02465 | 1.00900 | 0.99238 |
| 63 | 09956 | 09824 | 09430 | 08781 | 07891 | 06776 | 05459 | 03967 | 02334 | 1.00598 |
| 64 | 11701 | 11564 | 11154 | 10479 | 09553 | 08392 | 07020 | 05465 | 03762 | 01949 |
| 65 | 13446 | 13304 | 12878 | 12176 | 11213 | 10005 | 08577 | 06958 | 05183 | 03293 |
| 66 | 15192 | 15043 | 14601 | 13873 | 12871 | 11616 | 10132 | 08447 | 06599 | 04629 |
| 67 | 16937 | 16783 | 16324 | 15568 | 14529 | 13225 | 11683 | 09932 | 08009 | 05957 |
| 68 | 18682 | 18523 | 18047 | 17263 | 16185 | 14832 | 13231 | 11412 | 09413 | 07279 |
| 69 | 20428 | 20262 | 19769 | 18957 | 17839 | 16437 | 14776 | 12888 | 10812 | 08593 |
| 70 | 22173 | 22002 | 21491 | 20650 | 19493 | 18040 | 16318 | 14360 | 12205 | 09901 |
| 71 | 23918 | 23741 | 23213 | 22343 | 21145 | 19640 | 17857 | 15828 | 13594 | 11202 |
| 72 | 25664 | 25481 | 24935 | 24034 | 22796 | 21239 | 19394 | 17293 | 14977 | 12497 |
| 73 | 27409 | 27220 | 26656 | 25726 | 24446 | 22837 | 20928 | 18754 | 16356 | 13786 |
| 74 | 29154 | 28959 | 28377 | 27417 | 26094 | 24432 | 22459 | 20211 | 17731 | 15068 |
| 75 | 30900 | 30698 | 30097 | 29107 | 27742 | 26026 | 23989 | 21666 | 19101 | 16346 |
| 76 | 32645 | 32437 | 31818 | 30796 | 29389 | 27619 | 25516 | 23117 | 20467 | 17618 |
| 77 | 34390 | 34176 | 33538 | 32486 | 31035 | 29210 | 27041 | 24566 | 21830 | 18885 |
| 78 | 36136 | 35915 | 35258 | 34174 | 32680 | 30800 | 28565 | 26012 | 23189 | 20148 |
| 79 | 37881 | 37654 | 36978 | 35862 | 34325 | 32389 | 30086 | 27456 | 24544 | 21407 |
| 80 | 39626 | 39393 | 38698 | 37550 | 35968 | 33976 | 31606 | 28897 | 25897 | 22661 |
| 81 | 41372 | 41132 | 40417 | 39238 | 37611 | 35563 | 33124 | 30336 | 27246 | 23912 |
| 82 | 43117 | 42871 | 42137 | 40925 | 39254 | 37148 | 34641 | 31773 | 28594 | 25159 |
| 83 | 44862 | 44610 | 43856 | 42612 | 40896 | 38733 | 36157 | 33209 | 29939 | 26404 |
| 84 | 46608 | 46349 | 45575 | 44299 | 42537 | 40317 | 37672 | 34643 | 31282 | 27646 |
| 85 | 48353 | 48087 | 47294 | 45985 | 44178 | 41900 | 39186 | 36076 | 32623 | 28886 |
| 86 | 50098 | 49826 | 49013 | 47671 | 45819 | 43483 | 40699 | 37508 | 33963 | 30124 |
| 87 | 51844 | 51565 | 50732 | 49357 | 47459 | 45066 | 42211 | 38939 | 35302 | 31360 |
| 88 | 53589 | 53304 | 52451 | 51043 | 49100 | 46648 | 43723 | 40369 | 36640 | 32596 |
| 89 | 55334 | 55042 | 54170 | 52729 | 50740 | 48230 | 45235 | 41799 | 37977 | 33830 |
| 90 | 1.57080 | 1.56781 | 1.55889 | 1.54415 | 1.52380 | 1.49811 | 1.46746 | 1.43229 | 1.39314 | 1.35064 |

## III.—ELLIPTIC INTEGRALS OF THE SECOND KIND

| φ | θ 50° | 55° | 60° | 65° | 70° | 75° | 80° | 85° | 90° |
|---|---|---|---|---|---|---|---|---|---|
| 46° | 0.75599 | 0.74881 | 0.74195 | 0.73564 | 0.73010 | 0.72554 | 0.72215 | 0.72005 | 0.71934 |
| 47 | 77050 | 76285 | 75553 | 74879 | 74287 | 73800 | 73436 | 73211 | 73135 |
| 48 | 78490 | 77676 | 76896 | 76177 | 75546 | 75025 | 74636 | 74396 | 74314 |
| 49 | 79920 | 79054 | 78225 | 77459 | 76786 | 76230 | 75815 | 75558 | 75471 |
| 50 | 81338 | 80419 | 79538 | 78724 | 78007 | 77414 | 76971 | 76697 | 76604 |
| 51 | 82746 | 81772 | 80836 | 79971 | 79208 | 78578 | 78106 | 77814 | 77715 |
| 52 | 84143 | 83111 | 82120 | 81202 | 80391 | 79720 | 79218 | 78907 | 78801 |
| 53 | 85529 | 84438 | 83388 | 82415 | 81554 | 80842 | 80307 | 79976 | 79864 |
| 54 | 86904 | 85752 | 84641 | 83610 | 82698 | 81941 | 81374 | 81021 | 80902 |
| 55 | 88269 | 87052 | 85879 | 84788 | 83822 | 83020 | 82417 | 82042 | 81915 |
| 56 | 89622 | 88340 | 87101 | 85949 | 84926 | 84076 | 83436 | 83039 | 82904 |
| 57 | 90965 | 89614 | 88308 | 87092 | 86011 | 85110 | 84432 | 84010 | 83867 |
| 58 | 92297 | 90876 | 89500 | 88217 | 87075 | 86122 | 85404 | 84957 | 84805 |
| 59 | 93619 | 92125 | 90677 | 89325 | 88119 | 87112 | 86352 | 85878 | 85717 |
| 60 | 94930 | 93362 | 91839 | 90415 | 89144 | 88080 | 87276 | 86773 | 86603 |
| 61 | 96231 | 94586 | 92986 | 91488 | 90148 | 89025 | 88175 | 87643 | 87462 |
| 62 | 97521 | 95797 | 94118 | 92543 | 91132 | 89948 | 89049 | 88486 | 88295 |
| 63 | 0.98802 | 96996 | 95236 | 93581 | 92096 | 90848 | 89898 | 89303 | 89101 |
| 64 | 1.00072 | 98183 | 96339 | 94602 | 93041 | 91725 | 90273 | 90094 | 89879 |
| 65 | 01333 | 0.99358 | 97427 | 95606 | 93965 | 92580 | 91523 | 90858 | 90631 |
| 66 | 02585 | 1.00522 | 98502 | 96593 | 94870 | 93412 | 92297 | 91595 | 91355 |
| 67 | 03827 | 01674 | 0.99562 | 97564 | 95756 | 94222 | 93047 | 92305 | 92050 |
| 68 | 05060 | 02815 | 1.00609 | 98518 | 96622 | 95010 | 93771 | 92987 | 92718 |
| 69 | 06284 | 03945 | 01643 | 0.99456 | 97469 | 95775 | 94470 | 93642 | 93358 |
| 70 | 07500 | 05064 | 02664 | 1.00379 | 98298 | 96519 | 95144 | 94270 | 93969 |
| 71 | 08707 | 06173 | 03672 | 01286 | 99108 | 97240 | 95793 | 94870 | 94552 |
| 72 | 09907 | 07272 | 04668 | 02178 | 0.99900 | 97940 | 96417 | 95442 | 95106 |
| 73 | 11098 | 08362 | 05651 | 03056 | 1.00674 | 98619 | 97016 | 95987 | 95630 |
| 74 | 12283 | 09442 | 06624 | 03919 | 01431 | 99278 | 97590 | 96503 | 96126 |
| 75 | 13460 | 10513 | 07586 | 04769 | 02172 | 0.99916 | 98141 | 96992 | 96593 |
| 76 | 14631 | 11577 | 08537 | 05607 | 02896 | 1.00534 | 98667 | 97453 | 97030 |
| 77 | 15795 | 12632 | 09478 | 06432 | 03605 | 01133 | 99170 | 97887 | 97437 |
| 78 | 16954 | 13680 | 10410 | 07245 | 04300 | 01714 | 0.99650 | 98293 | 97815 |
| 79 | 18107 | 14721 | 11333 | 08047 | 04981 | 02277 | 1.00107 | 98671 | 98163 |
| 80 | 19255 | 15755 | 12249 | 08839 | 05648 | 02823 | 00543 | 99023 | 98481 |
| 81 | 20399 | 16784 | 13156 | 09621 | 06304 | 03354 | 00958 | 99348 | 98769 |
| 82 | 21538 | 17807 | 14057 | 10395 | 06948 | 03870 | 01354 | 99646 | 99027 |
| 83 | 22673 | 18825 | 14952 | 11161 | 07582 | 04372 | 01731 | 0.99920 | 99255 |
| 84 | 23805 | 19839 | 15841 | 11920 | 08207 | 04863 | 02091 | 1.00168 | 99452 |
| 85 | 24934 | 20850 | 16726 | 12673 | 08825 | 05343 | 02436 | 00394 | 99619 |
| 86 | 26061 | 21857 | 17606 | 13421 | 09435 | 05813 | 02768 | 00598 | 99756 |
| 87 | 27186 | 22862 | 18484 | 14165 | 10041 | 06277 | 03089 | 00784 | 99863 |
| 88 | 28310 | 23865 | 19359 | 14906 | 10642 | 06735 | 03401 | 00954 | 99939 |
| 89 | 29432 | 24867 | 20233 | 15645 | 11241 | 07188 | 03708 | 01113 | 0.99985 |
| 90 | 1.30554 | 1.25868 | 1.21106 | 1.16383 | 1.11838 | 1.07641 | 1.04011 | 1.01266 | 1.00000 |

# INDEX

# Catalogue of Dover
## SCIENCE BOOKS

### DIFFERENTIAL EQUATIONS
### (ORDINARY AND PARTIAL DIFFERENTIAL)

**INTRODUCTION TO THE DIFFERENTIAL EQUATIONS OF PHYSICS, L. Hopf.** Especially valuable to engineer with no math beyond elementary calculus. Emphasizes intuitive rather than formal aspects of concepts. Partial contents: Law of causality, energy theorem, damped oscillations, coupling by friction, cylindrical and spherical coordinates, heat source, etc. 48 figures. 160pp. 5⅜ x 8.　　　　　　　　　　　　　　　　　　　　　　S120 Paperbound **$1.25**

**INTRODUCTION TO BESSEL FUNCTIONS, F. Bowman.** Rigorous, provides all necessary material during development, includes practical applications. Bessel functions of zero order, of any real order, definite integrals, asymptotic expansion, circular membranes, Bessel's solution to Kepler's problem, much more. "Clear . . . useful not only to students of physics and engineering, but to mathematical students in general," Nature. 226 problems. Short tables of Bessel functions. 27 figures. x + 135pp. 5⅜ x 8.　　　　　　　　S462 Paperbound **$1.35**

**DIFFERENTIAL EQUATIONS, F. R. Moulton.** Detailed, rigorous exposition of all non-elementary processes of solving ordinary differential equations. Chapters on practical problems; more advanced than problems usually given as illustrations. Includes analytic differential equations; variations of a parameter; integrals of differential equations; analytic implicit functions; problems of elliptic motion; sine-amplitude functions; deviation of formal bodies; Cauchy-Lipshitz process; linear differential equations with periodic coefficients; much more. Historical notes. 10 figures. 222 problems. xv + 395pp. 5⅜ x 8.　　S451 Paperbound **$2.00**

**PARTIAL DIFFERENTIAL EQUATIONS OF MATHEMATICAL PHYSICS, A. G. Webster.** Valuable sections on elasticity, compression theory, potential theory, theory of sound, heat conduction, wave propagation, vibration theory. Contents include: deduction of differential equations, vibrations, normal functions, Fourier's series. Cauchy's method, boundary problems, method of Riemann-Volterra, spherical, cylindrical, ellipsoidal harmonics, applications, etc. 97 figures. vii + 440pp. 5⅜ x 8.　　　　　　　　　　　　　S263 Paperbound **$2.00**

**ORDINARY DIFFERENTIAL EQUATIONS, E. L. Ince.** A most compendious analysis in real and complex domains. Existence and nature of solutions, continuous transformation groups, solutions in an infinite form, definite integrals, algebraic theory. Sturmian theory, boundary problems, existence theorems, 1st order, higher order, etc. "Deserves highest praise, a notable addition to mathematical literature," Bulletin, Amer. Math. Soc. Historical appendix. 18 figures. viii + 558pp. 5⅜ x 8.　　　　　　　　　　　　S349 Paperbound **$2.55**

**ASYMPTOTIC EXPANSIONS, A. Erdélyi.** Only modern work available in English; unabridged reproduction of monograph prepared for Office of Naval Research. Discusses various procedures for asymptotic evaluation of integrals containing a large parameter; solutions of ordinary linear differential equations. vi + 108pp. 5⅜ x 8.　　　S318 Paperbound **$1.35**

**LECTURES ON CAUCHY'S PROBLEM, J. Hadamard.** Based on lectures given at Columbia, Rome, discusses work of Riemann, Kirchhoff, Volterra, and author's own research on hyperbolic case in linear partial differential equations. Extends spherical cylindrical waves to apply to all (normal) hyperbolic equations. Partial contents: Cauchy's problem, fundamental formula, equations with odd number, with even number of independent variables; method of descent. 32 figures. iii + 316pp. 5⅜ x 8.　　　　　　　S105 Paperbound **$1.75**

## NUMBER THEORY

**INTRODUCTION TO THE THEORY OF NUMBERS, L. E. Dickson.** Thorough, comprehensive, with adequate coverage of classical literature. Not beyond beginners. Chapters on divisibility, congruences, quadratic residues and reciprocity, Diophantine equations, etc. Full treatment of binary quadratic forms without usual restriction to integral coefficients. Covers infinitude of primes, Fermat's theorem, Legendre's symbol, automorphs, Recent theorems of Thue, Siegal, much more. Much material not readily available elsewhere. 239 problems. 1 figure. viii + 183pp. 5⅜ x 8.                                                                    S342 Paperbound **$1.65**

**ELEMENTS OF NUMBER THEORY, I. M. Vinogradov.** Detailed 1st course for persons without advanced mathematics; 95% of this book can be understood by readers who have gone no farther than high school algebra. Partial contents: divisibility theory, important number theoretical functions, congruences, primitive roots and indices, etc. Solutions to problems, exercises. Tables of primes, indices, etc. Covers almost every essential formula in elementary number theory! "Welcome addition . . . reads smoothly," Bull. of the Amer. Math. Soc. 233 problems. 104 exercises. viii + 227pp. 5⅜ x 8.                          S259 Paperbound **$1.60**

## PROBABILITY THEORY AND INFORMATION THEORY

**SELECTED PAPERS ON NOISE AND STOCHASTIC PROCESSES,** edited by Prof. Nelson Wax, U. of Illinois. 6 basic papers for those whose work involves noise characteristics. Chandrasekhar, Uhlenback and Ornstein, Uhlenbeck and Ming, Rice, Doob. Included is Kac's Chauvenet-Prize winning "Random Walk." Extensive bibliography lists 200 articles, through 1953. 21 figures. 337pp. 6⅛ x 9¼.                                                                          S262 Paperbound **$2.35**

**A PHILOSOPHICAL ESSAY ON PROBABILITIES, Marquis de Laplace.** This famous essay explains without recourse to mathematics the principle of probability, and the application of probability to games of chance, natural philosophy, astronomy, many other fields. Translated from 6th French edition by F. W. Truscott, F. L. Emory. Intro. by E. T. Bell. 204pp. 5⅜ x 8.                                                                                          S166 Paperbound **$1.25**

**MATHEMATICAL FOUNDATIONS OF INFORMATION THEORY, A. I. Khinchin.** For mathematicians, statisticians, physicists, cyberneticists, communications engineers, a complete, exact introduction to relatively new field. Entropy as a measure of a finite scheme, applications to coding theory, study of sources, channels and codes, detailed proofs of both Shannon theorems for any ergodic source and any stationary channel with finite memory, much more. "Presents for the first time rigorous proofs of certain fundamental theorems . . . quite complete . . . amazing expository ability," American Math. Monthly. vii + 120pp. 5⅜ x 8.                                                                                          S434 Paperbound **$1.35**

## VECTOR AND TENSOR ANALYSIS AND MATRIX THEORY

**VECTOR AND TENSOR ANALYSIS, G. E. Hay.** One of clearest introductions to increasingly important subject. Start with simple definitions, finish with sure mastery of oriented Cartesian vectors, Christoffel symbols, solenoidal tensors. Complete breakdown of plane, solid, analytical, differential geometry. Separate chapters on application. All fundamental formulae listed, demonstrated. 195 problems. 66 figures. viii + 193pp. 5⅜ x 8.                                                                                          S109 Paperbound **$1.75**

**APPLICATIONS OF TENSOR ANALYSIS, A. J. McConnell.** Excellent text for applying tensor methods to such familiar subjects as dynamics, electricity, elasticity, hydrodynamics. Explains fundamental ideas and notation of tensor theory, geometrical treatment of tensor algebra, theory of differentiation of tensors, and a wealth of practical material. "The variety of fields treated and the presence of extremely numerous examples make this volume worth much more than its low price," Alluminio. Formerly titled "Applications of the Absolute Differential Calculus." 43 illustrations. 685 problems. xii + 381pp.                                                                                          S373 Paperbound **$1.85**

**VECTOR AND TENSOR ANALYSIS, A. P. Wills.** Covers entire field, from dyads to non-Euclidean manifolds (especially detailed), absolute differentiation, the Riemann-Christoffel and Ricci-Einstein tensors, calculation of Gaussian curvature of a surface. Illustrations from electrical engineering, relativity theory, astro-physics, quantum mechanics. Presupposes only working knowledge of calculus. Intended for physicists, engineers, mathematicians. 44 diagrams. 114 problems. xxxii + 285pp. 5⅜ x 8.                                         S454 Paperbound **$1.75**

## PHYSICS, ENGINEERING

### MECHANICS, DYNAMICS, THERMODYNAMICS, ELASTICITY

**MATHEMATICAL ANALYSIS OF ELECTRICAL AND OPTICAL WAVE-MOTION, H. Bateman.** By one of century's most distinguished mathematical physicists, a practical introduction to developments of Maxwell's electromagnetic theory which directly concern the solution of partial differential equation of wave motion. Methods of solving wave-equation, polar-cylindrical coordinates, diffraction, transformation of coordinates, homogeneous solutions, electromagnetic fields with moving singularities, etc. 168pp. 5⅜ x 8. S14 Paperbound **$1.60**

**THERMODYNAMICS, Enrico Fermi.** Unabridged reproduction of 1937 edition. Remarkable for clarity, organization; requires no knowledge of advanced math beyond calculus, only familiarity with fundamentals of thermometry, calorimetry. Partial Contents: Thermodynamic systems, 1st and 2nd laws, potentials; Entropy, phase rule; Reversible electric cells; Gaseous reactions: Van't Hoff reaction box, principle of LeChatelier; Thermodynamics of dilute solutions: osmotic, vapor pressures; boiling, freezing point; Entropy constant. 25 problems. 24 illustrations. x + 160pp. 5⅜ x 8. S361 Paperbound **$1.75**

**FOUNDATIONS OF POTENTIAL THEORY, O. D. Kellogg.** Based on courses given at Harvard, suitable for both advanced and beginning mathematicians. Proofs rigorous, much material here not generally available elsewhere. Partial contents: gravity, fields of force, divergence theorem, properties of Newtonian potentials at points of free space, potentials as solutions of LaPlace's equation, harmonic functions, electrostatics, electric images, logarithmic potential, etc. ix + 384pp. 5⅜ x 8. S144 Paperbound **$1.98**

**DIALOGUES CONCERNING TWO NEW SCIENCES, Galileo Galilei.** Classic of experimental science, mechanics, engineering, as enjoyable as it is important. Characterized by author as "superior to everything else of mine." Offers a lively exposition of dynamics, elasticity, sound, ballistics, strength of materials, scientific method. Translated by H. Grew, A. de Salvio. 126 diagrams. xxi + 288pp. 5⅜ x 8. S99 Paperbound **$1.65**

**THEORETICAL MECHANICS; AN INTRODUCTION TO MATHEMATICAL PHYSICS, J. S. Ames, F. D. Murnaghan.** A mathematically rigorous development for advanced students, with constant practical applications. Used in hundreds of advanced courses. Unusually thorough coverage of gyroscopic baryscopic material, detailed analyses of Corilis acceleration, applications of Lagrange's equations, motion of double pendulum, Hamilton-Jacobi partial differential equations, group velocity, dispersion, etc. Special relativity included. 159 problems. 44 figures. ix + 462pp. 5⅜ x 8. S461 Paperbound **$2.00**

**STATICS AND THE DYNAMICS OF A PARTICLE, W. D. MacMillan.** This is Part One of "Theoretical Mechanics." For over 3 decades a self-contained, extremely comprehensive advanced undergraduate text in mathematical physics, physics, astronomy, deeper foundations of engineering. Early sections require only a knowledge of geometry; later, a working knowledge of calculus. Hundreds of basic problems including projectiles to moon, harmonic motion, ballistics, transmission of power, stress and strain, elasticity, astronomical problems. 340 practice problems, many fully worked out examples. 200 figures. xvii + 430pp. 5⅜ x 8. S467 Paperbound **$2.00**

**THE THEORY OF THE POTENTIAL, W. D. MacMillan.** This is Part Two of "Theoretical Mechanics." Comprehensive, well-balanced presentation, serving both as introduction and reference with regard to specific problems, for physicists and mathematicians. Assumes no prior knowledge of integral relations, all math is developed as needed. Includes: Attraction of Finite Bodies; Newtonian Potential Function; Vector Fields, Green and Gauss Theorems; Two-layer Surfaces; Spherical Harmonics; etc. "The great number of particular cases . . . should make the book valuable to geo-physicists and others actively engaged in practical applications of the potential theory," Review of Scientific Instruments. xii + 469pp. 5⅜ x 8. S486 Paperbound **$2.25**

**DYNAMICS OF A SYSTEM OF RIGID BODIES (Advanced Section), E. J. Routh.** Revised 6th edition of a classic reference aid. Partial contents: moving axes, relative motion, oscillations about equilibrium, motion. Motion of a body under no forces, any forces. Nature of motion given by linear equations and conditions of stability. Free, forced vibrations, constants of integration, calculus of finite differences, variations, procession and mutation, motion of the moon, motion of string, chain, membranes. 64 figures. 498pp. 5⅜ x 8. S229 Paperbound **$2.35**

**THE DYNAMICS OF PARTICLES AND OF RIGID, ELASTIC, AND FLUID BODIES: BEING LECTURES ON MATHEMATICAL PHYSICS, A. G. Webster.** Reissuing of classic fills need for comprehensive work on dynamics. Covers wide range in unusually great depth, applying ordinary, partial differential equations. Partial contents: laws of motion, methods applicable to systems of all sorts; oscillation, resonance, cyclic systems; dynamics of rigid bodies; potential theory; stress and strain; gyrostatics; wave, vortex motion; kinematics of a point; Lagrange's equations; Hamilton's principle; vectors; deformable bodies; much more not easily found together in one volume. Unabridged reprinting of 2nd edition. 20 pages on differential equations, higher analysis. 203 illustrations. xi + 588pp. 5⅜ x 8. S522 Paperbound **$2.35**

**PRINCIPLES OF MECHANICS, Heinrich Hertz.** A classic of great interest in logic of science. Last work by great 19th century physicist, created new system of mechanics based upon space, time, mass; returns to axiomatic analysis, understanding of formal, structural aspects of science, taking into account logic, observation, a priori elements. Of great historical importance to Poincaré, Carnap, Einstein, Milne. 20 page introduction by R. S. Cohen, Wesleyan U., analyzes implications of Hertz's thought and logic of science. 13 page introduction by Helmholtz. xlii + 274pp. 5⅜ x 8.　　　　　　　　S316 Clothbound **$3.50**
　　　　　　　　　　　　　　　　　　　　　　　　　　　　　　　　　S317 Paperbound **$1.75**

**MATHEMATICAL FOUNDATIONS OF STATISTICAL MECHANICS, A. I. Khinchin.** A thoroughly up-to-date introduction, offering a precise and mathematically rigorous formulation of the problems of statistical mechanics. Provides analytical tools to replace many commonly used cumbersome concepts and devices. Partial contents: Geometry, kinematics of phase space; ergodic problem; theory of probability; central limit theorem; ideal monatomic gas; foundation of thermodynamics; dispersion, distribution of sum functions; etc. "Excellent introduction . . . clear, concise, rigorous," Quarterly of Applied Mathematics. viii + 179pp. 5⅜ x 8.　　　　　　　　　　　　　　　　　　　　　　　S146 Clothbound **$2.95**
　　　　　　　　　　　　　　　　　　　　　　　　　　　　　　　　　S147 Paperbound **$1.35**

**MECHANICS OF THE GYROSCOPE, THE DYNAMICS OF ROTATION, R. F. Deimel,** Prof. of Mechanical Engineering, Stevens Inst. of Tech. Elementary, general treatment of dynamics of rotation, with special application of gyroscopic phenomena. No knowledge of vectors needed. Velocity of a moving curve, acceleration to a point, general equations of motion, gyroscopic horizon, free gyro, motion of discs, the damped gyro, 103 similar topics. Exercises. 75 figures. 208pp. 5⅜ x 8.　　　　　　　　　　　S66 Paperbound **$1.65**

**MECHANICS VIA THE CALCULUS, P. W. Norris, W. S. Legge.** Wide coverage, from linear motion to vector analysis; equations determining motion, linear methods, compounding of simple harmonic motions, Newton's laws of motion, Hooke's law, the simple pendulum, motion of a particle in 1 plane, centers of gravity, virtual work, friction, kinetic energy of rotating bodies, equilibrium of strings, hydrostatics, sheering stresses, elasticity, etc. Many worked-out examples. 550 problems. 3rd revised edition. xii + 367pp.　　　S207 Clothbound **$3.95**

**A TREATISE ON THE MATHEMATICAL THEORY OF ELASTICITY, A. E. H. Love.** An indispensable reference work for engineers, mathematicians, physicists, the most complete, authoritative treatment of classical elasticity in one volume. Proceeds from elementary notions of extension to types of strain, cubical dilatation, general theory of strains. Covers relation between mathematical theory of elasticity and technical mechanics; equilibrium of isotropic elastic solids and aelotropic solid bodies; nature of force transmission, Volterra's theory of dislocations; theory of elastic spheres in relation to tidal, rotational, gravitational effects on earth; general theory of bending; deformation of curved plates; buckling effects; much more. "The standard treatise on elasticity," American Math. Monthly. 4th revised edition. 76 figures. xviii + 643pp. 6⅛ x 9¼.　　　　　　　　　　S174 Paperbound **$2.95**

# NUCLEAR PHYSICS, QUANTUM THEORY, RELATIVITY

**MESON PHYSICS, R. E. Marshak.** Presents basic theory, and results of experiments with emphasis on theoretical significance. Phenomena involving mesons as virtual transitions avoided, eliminating some of least satisfactory predictions of meson theory. Includes production study of $\pi$ mesons at nonrelativistic nucleon energies contracts between $\pi$ and $u$ mesons, phenomena associated with nuclear interaction of $\pi$ mesons, etc. Presents early evidence for new classes of particles, indicates theoretical difficulties created by discovery of heavy mesons and hyperons. viii + 378pp. 5⅜ x 8.　　　　S500 Paperbound **$1.95**

**THE FUNDAMENTAL PRINCIPLES OF QUANTUM MECHANICS, WITH ELEMENTARY APPLICATIONS, E. C. Kemble.** Inductive presentation, for graduate student, specialists in other branches of physics. Apparatus necessary beyond differential equations and advanced calculus developed as needed. Though general exposition of principles, hundreds of individual problems fully treated. "Excellent book . . . of great value to every student . . . rigorous and detailed mathematical discussion . .. has succeeded in keeping his presentation clear and understandable," Dr. Linus Pauling, J. of American Chemical Society. Appendices: calculus of variations, math. notes, etc. 611pp. 5⅝ x 8⅜.　　　　　　T472 Paperbound **$2.95**

**WAVE PROPAGATION IN PERIODIC STRUCTURES, L. Brillouin.** General method, application to different problems: pure physics—scattering of X-rays in crystals, thermal vibration in crystal lattices, electronic motion in metals; problems in electrical engineering. Partial contents: elastic waves along 1-dimensional lattices of point masses. Propagation of waves along 1-dimensional lattices. Energy flow. 2, 3 dimensional lattices. Mathieu's equation. Matrices and propagation of waves along an electric line. Continuous electric lines. 131 illustrations. xii + 253pp. 5⅜ x 8.　　　　　　　　　　S34 Paperbound **$1.85**

**THEORY OF ELECTRONS AND ITS APPLICATION TO THE PHENOMENA OF LIGHT AND RADIANT HEAT, H. Lorentz.** Lectures delivered at Columbia Univ., by Nobel laureate. Unabridged, form historical coverage of theory of free electrons, motion, absorption of heat, Zeeman effect, optical phenomena in moving bodies, etc. 109 pages notes explain more advanced sections. 9 figures. 352pp. 5⅜ x 8. S173 Paperbound **$1.85**

**SELECTED PAPERS ON QUANTUM ELECTRODYNAMICS, edited by J. Schwinger.** Facsimiles of papers which established quantum electrodynamics; beginning to present position as part of larger theory. First book publication in any language of collected papers of Bethe, Bloch, Dirac, Dyson, Fermi, Feynman, Heisenberg, Kusch, Lamb, Oppenheimer, Pauli, Schwinger, Tomonoga, Weisskopf, Wigner, etc. 34 papers: 29 in English, 1 in French, 3 in German, 1 in Italian. Historical commentary by editor. xvii + 423pp. 6⅛ x 9¼.
S444 Paperbound **$2.45**

**FOUNDATIONS OF NUCLEAR PHYSICS, edited by R. T. Beyer.** 13 of the most important papers on nuclear physics reproduced in facsimile in the original languages; the papers most often cited in footnotes, bibliographies. Anderson, Curie, Joliot, Chadwick, Fermi, Lawrence, Cockroft, Hahn, Yukawa. Unparalleled bibliography: 122 double columned pages, over 4,000 articles, books, classified. 57 figures. 288pp. 6⅛ x 9¼. S19 Paperbound **$1.75**

**THE THEORY OF GROUPS AND QUANTUM MECHANICS, H. Weyl.** Schroedinger's wave equation, de Broglie's waves of a particle, Jordon-Hoelder theorem, Lie's continuous groups of transformations, Pauli exclusion principle, quantization of Mawell-Dirac field equations, etc. Unitary geometry, quantum theory, groups, application of groups to quantum mechanics, symmetry permutation group, algebra of symmetric transformations, etc. 2nd revised edition. xxii + 422pp. 5⅜ x 8. S268 Clothbound **$4.50**
S269 Paperbound **$1.95**

**PHYSICAL PRINCIPLES OF THE QUANTUM THEORY, Werner Heisenberg.** Nobel laureate discusses quantum theory; his own work, Compton, Schroedinger, Wilson, Einstein, many others. For physicists, chemists, not specialists in quantum theory. Only elementary formulae considered in text; mathematical appendix for specialists. Profound without sacrificing clarity. Translated by C. Eckart, F. Hoyt. 18 figures. 192pp. 5⅜ x 8.
S113 Paperbound **$1.25**

**INVESTIGATIONS ON THE THEORY OF THE BROWNIAN MOVEMENT, Albert Einstein.** Reprints from rare European journals, translated into English. 5 basic papers, including Elementary Theory of the Brownian Movement, written at request of Lorentz to provide a simple explanation. Translated by A. D. Cowper. Annotated, edited by R. Fürth. 33pp. of notes elucidate, give history of previous investigations. 62 footnotes. 124pp. 5⅜ x 8.
S304 Paperbound **$1.25**

**THE PRINCIPLE OF RELATIVITY, E. Einstein, H. Lorentz, M. Minkowski, H. Weyl.** The 11 basic papers that founded the general and special theories of relativity, translated into English. 2 papers by Lorentz on the Michelson experiment, electromagnetic phenomena. Minkowski's "Space and Time," and Weyl's "Gravitation and Electricity." 7 epoch-making papers by Einstein: "Electromagnetics of Moving Bodies," "Influence of Gravitation in Propagation of Light," "Cosmological Considerations," "General Theory," 3 others. 7 diagrams. Special notes by A. Sommerfeld. 224pp. 5⅜ x 8. S93 Paperbound **$1.75**

## STATISTICS

**ELEMENTARY STATISTICS, WITH APPLICATIONS IN MEDICINE AND THE BIOLOGICAL SCIENCES, F. E. Croxton.** Based primarily on biological sciences, but can be used by anyone desiring introduction to statistics. Assumes no prior acquaintance, requires only modest knowledge of math. All basic formulas carefully explained, illustrated; all necessary reference tables included. From basic terms and concepts, proceeds to frequency distribution, linear, non-linear, multiple correlation, etc. Contains concrete examples from medicine, biology. 101 charts. 57 tables. 14 appendices. lv + 376pp. 5⅜ x 8. S506 Paperbound **$1.95**

**ANALYSIS AND DESIGN OF EXPERIMENTS, H. B. Mann.** Offers method for grasping analysis of variance, variance design quickly. Partial contents: Chi-square distribution, analysis of variance distribution, matrices, quadratic forms, likelihood ration tests, test of linear hypotheses, power of analysis, Galois fields, non-orthogonal data, interblock estimates, etc. 15pp. of useful tables. x + 195pp. 5 x 7⅜. S180 Paperbound **$1.45**

**FREQUENCY CURVES AND CORRELATION, W. P. Elderton.** 4th revised edition of standard work on classical statistics. Practical, one of few books constantly referred to for clear presentation of basic material. Partial contents: Frequency Distributions; Pearsons Frequency Curves; Theoretical Distributions; Standard Errors; Correlation Ratio—Contingency; Corrections for Moments, Beta, Gamma Functions; etc. Key to terms, symbols. 25 examples. 40 tables. 16 figures. xi + 272pp. 5½ x 8½. Clothbound **$1.49**

## HYDRODYNAMICS, ETC.

**HYDRODYNAMICS, Horace Lamb.** Standard reference work on dynamics of liquids and gases. Fundamental theorems, equations, methods, solutions, background for classical hydrodynamics. Chapters: Equations of Motion, Integration of Equations in Special Gases, Vortex Motion, Tidal Waves, Rotating Masses of Liquids, etc. Excellently planned, arranged, Clear, lucid presentation. 6th enlarged, revised edition. Over 900 footnotes, mostly bibliographical. 119 figures. xv + 738pp. 6⅛ x 9¼. S256 Paperbound **$2.95**

**HYDRODYNAMICS, A STUDY OF LOGIC, FACT, AND SIMILITUDE, Garrett Birkhoff.** A stimulating application of pure mathematics to an applied problem. Emphasis is on correlation of theory and deduction with experiment. Examines recently discovered paradoxes, theory of modelling and dimensional analysis, paradox and error in flows and free boundary theory. Classical theory of virtual mass derived from homogenous spaces; group theory applied to fluid mechanics. 20 figures, 3 plates. xiii + 186pp. 5⅜ x 8. S22 Paperbound **$1.85**

**HYDRODYNAMICS, H. Dryden, F. Murhaghan, H. Bateman.** Published by National Research Council, 1932. Complete coverage of classical hydrodynamics, encyclopedic in quality. Partial contents: physics of fluids, motion, turbulent flow, compressible fluids, motion in 1, 2, 3 dimensions; laminar motion, resistance of motion through viscous fluid, eddy viscosity, discharge of gases, flow past obstacles, etc. Over 2900-item bibliography. 23 figures. 634pp. 5⅜ x 8. S303 Paperbound **$2.75**

## ACOUSTICS AND OPTICS

**PRINCIPLES OF PHYSICAL OPTICS, Ernst Mach.** Classical examination of propagation of light, color, polarization, etc. Historical, philosophical treatment unequalled for breadth and readability. Contents: Rectilinear propagation, reflection, refraction, dioptrics, composition of light, periodicity, theory of interference, polarization, mathematical representation of properties, etc. 279 illustrations. 10 portraits. 324pp. 5⅜ x 8. S170 Paperbound **$1.75**

**THE THEORY OF SOUND, Lord Rayleigh.** Written by Nobel laureate, classical methods here will cover most vibrating systems likely to be encountered in practice. Complete coverage of experimental, mathematical aspects. Partial contents: Harmonic motions, lateral vibrations of bars, curved plates or shells, applications of Laplace's functions to acoustical problems, fluid friction, etc. First low-priced edition of this great reference-study work. Historical introduction by R. B. Lindsay. 1040pp. 97 figures. 5⅜ x 8.
S292, S293, Two volume set, paperbound **$4.00**

**THEORY OF VIBRATIONS, N. W. McLachlan.** Based on exceptionally successful graduate course, Brown University. Discusses linear systems having 1 degree of freedom, forced vibrations of simple linear systems, vibration of flexible strings, transverse vibrations of bars and tubes, of circular plate, sound waves of finite amplitude, etc. 99 diagrams. 160pp. 5⅜ x 8. S190 Paperbound **$1.35**

**APPLIED OPTICS AND OPTICAL DESIGN, A. E. Conrady.** Thorough systematic presentation of physical and mathematical aspects, limited mostly to "real optics." Stresses practical problem of maximum aberration permissible without affecting performance. Ordinary ray tracing methods; complete theory ray tracing methods, primary aberrations; enough higher aberration to design telescopes, low powered microscopes, photographic equipment. Covers fundamental equations, extra-axial image points, transverse chromatic aberration, angular magnification, similar topics. Tables of functions of N. Over 150 diagrams. x + 518pp. 5⅜ x 8⅝. S366 Paperbound **$2.98**

**RAYLEIGH'S PRINCIPLE AND ITS APPLICATIONS TO ENGINEERING, G. Temple, W. Bickley.** Rayleigh's principle developed to provide upper, lower estimates of true value of fundamental period of vibrating system, or condition of stability of elastic system. Examples, rigorous proofs. Partial contents: Energy method of discussing vibrations, stability. Perturbation theory, whirling of uniform shafts. Proof, accuracy, successive approximations, applications of Rayleigh's theory. Numerical, graphical methods. Ritz's method. 22 figures. ix + 156pp. 5⅜ x 8. S307 Paperbound **$1.50**

**OPTICKS, Sir Isaac Newton.** In its discussion of light, reflection, color, refraction, theories of wave and corpuscular theories of light, this work is packed with scores of insights and discoveries. In its precise and practical discussions of construction of optical apparatus, contemporary understanding of phenomena, it is truly fascinating to modern scientists. Foreword by Albert Einstein. Preface by I. B. Cohen, Harvard. 7 pages of portraits, facsimile pages, letters, etc. cxvi + 414pp. 5⅜ x 8. S205 Paperbound **$2.00**

# DOVER SCIENCE BOOKS

**ON THE SENSATIONS OF TONE, Hermann Helmholtz.** Using acoustical physics, physiology, experiment, history of music, covers entire gamut of musical tone: relation of music science to acoustics, physical vs. physiological acoustics, vibration, resonance, tonality, progression of parts, etc. 33 appendixes on various aspects of sound, physics, acoustics, music, etc. Translated by A. J. Ellis. New introduction by H. Margenau, Yale. 68 figures. 43 musical passages analyzed. Over 100 tables. xix + 576pp. 6⅛ x 9¼.
S114 Clothbound **$4.95**

## ELECTROMAGNETICS, ENGINEERING, TECHNOLOGY

**INTRODUCTION TO RELAXATION METHODS, F. S. Shaw.** Describes almost all manipulative resources of value in solution of differential equations. Treatment is mathematical rather than physical. Extends general computational process to include almost all branches of applied math and physics. Approximate numerical methods are demonstrated, although high accuracy is obtainable without undue expenditure of time. 48pp. of tables for computing irregular star first and second derivatives, irregular star coefficients for second order equations, for fourth order equations. "Useful. . . . exposition is clear, simple . . . no previous acquaintance with numerical methods is assumed," Science Progress. 253 diagrams. 72 tables. 400pp. 5⅜ x 8.
S244 Paperbound **$2.45**

**THE ELECTROMAGNETIC FIELD, M. Mason, W. Weaver.** Used constantly by graduate engineers. Vector methods exclusively; detailed treatment of electrostatics, expansion methods, with tables converting any quantity into absolute electromagnetic, absolute electrostatic, practical units. Discrete charges, ponderable bodies. Maxwell field equations, etc. 416pp. 5⅜ x 8.
S185 Paperbound **$2.00**

**ELASTICITY, PLASTICITY AND STRUCTURE OF MATTER, R. Houwink.** Standard treatise on rheological aspects of different technically important solids: crystals, resins, textiles, rubber, clay, etc. Investigates general laws for deformations; determines divergences. Covers general physical and mathematical aspects of plasticity, elasticity, viscosity. Detailed examination of deformations, internal structure of matter in relation to elastic, plastic behaviour, formation of solid matter from a fluid, etc. Treats glass, asphalt, balata, proteins, baker's dough, others. 2nd revised, enlarged edition. Extensive revised bibliography in over 500 footnotes. 214 figures. xvii + 368pp. 6 x 9¼.
S385 Paperbound **$2.45**

**DESIGN AND USE OF INSTRUMENTS AND ACCURATE MECHANISM, T. N. Whitehead.** For the instrument designer, engineer; how to combine necessary mathematical abstractions with independent observations of actual facts. Partial contents: instruments and their parts, theory of errors, systematic errors, probability, short period errors, erratic errors, design precision, kinematic, semikinematic design, stiffness, planning of an instrument, human factor, etc. 85 photos, diagrams. xii + 288pp. 5⅜ x 8.
S270 Paperbound **$1.95**

**APPLIED HYDRO- AND AEROMECHANICS, L. Prandtl, O. G. Tietjens.** Presents, for most part, methods valuable to engineers. Flow in pipes, boundary layers, airfoil theory, entry conditions, turbulent flow, boundary layer, determining drag from pressure and velocity, etc. "Will be welcomed by all students of aerodynamics," Nature. Unabridged, unaltered. An Engineering Society Monograph, 1934. Index. 226 figures. 28 photographic plates illustrating flow patterns. xvi + 311pp. 5⅜ x 8.
S375 Paperbound **$1.85**

**FUNDAMENTALS OF HYDRO- AND AEROMECHANICS, L. Prandtl, O. G. Tietjens.** Standard work, based on Prandtl's lectures at Goettingen. Wherever possible hydrodynamics theory is referred to practical considerations in hydraulics, unifying theory and experience. Presentation extremely clear. Though primarily physical, proofs are rigorous and use vector analysis to a great extent. An Engineering Society Monograph, 1934. "Still recommended as an excellent introduction to this area," Physikalische Blätter. 186 figures. xvi + 270pp. 5⅜ x 8.
S374 Paperbound **$1.85**

**GASEOUS CONDUCTORS: THEORY AND ENGINEERING APPLICATIONS, J. D. Cobine.** Indispensable text, reference, to gaseous conduction phenomena, with engineering viewpoint prevailing throughout. Studies kinetic theory of gases, ionization, emission phenomena; gas breakdown, spark characteristics, glow, discharges; engineering applications in circuit interrupters, rectifiers, etc. Detailed treatment of high pressure arcs (Suits); low pressure arcs (Langmuir, Tonks). Much more. "Well organized, clear, straightforward," Tonks, Review of Scientific Instruments. 83 practice problems. Over 600 figures. 58 tables. xx + 606pp. 5⅜ x 8.
S442 Paperbound **$2.75**

**PHOTOELASTICITY: PRINCIPLES AND METHODS, H. T. Jessop, F. C. Harris.** For engineer, specific problems of stress analysis. Latest time-saving methods of checking calculations in 2-dimensional design problems, new techniques for stresses in 3 dimensions, lucid description of optical systems used in practical photoelectricity. Useful suggestions, hints based on on-the-job experience included. Partial contents: strain, stress-strain relations, circular disc under thrust along diameter, rectangular block with square hold under vertical thrust, simply supported rectangular beam under central concentrated load, etc. Theory held to minimum, no advanced mathematical training needed. 164 illustrations. viii + 184pp. 6⅛ x 9¼.
S137 Clothbound **$3.75**

**MICROWAVE TRANSMISSION DESIGN DATA, T. Moreno.** Originally classified, now rewritten, enlarged (14 new chapters) under auspices of Sperry Corp. Of immediate value or reference use to radio engineers, systems designers, applied physicists, etc. Ordinary transmission line theory; attenuation; parameters of coaxial lines; flexible cables; tuneable wave guide impedance transformers; effects of temperature, humidity; much more. "Packed with information . . . theoretical discussions are directly related to practical questions," U. of Royal Naval Scientific Service. Tables of dielectrics, flexible cable, etc. ix + 248pp. 5⅜ x 8.
S549 Paperbound **$1.50**

**THE THEORY OF THE PROPERTIES OF METALS AND ALLOYS, H. F. Mott, H. Jones.** Quantum methods develop mathematical models showing interrelationship of fundamental chemical phenomena wtih crystal structure, electrical, optical properties, etc. Examines electron motion in applied field, cohesion, heat capacity, refraction, noble metals, transition and di-valent metals, etc. "Exposition is as clear . . . mathematical treatment as simple and reliable as we have become used to expect of . . . Prof. Mott," Nature. 138 figures. xiii + 320pp. 5⅜ x 8.
S456 Paperbound **$1.85**

**THE MEASUREMENT OF POWER SPECTRA FROM THE POINT OF VIEW OF COMMUNICATIONS ENGINEERING, R. B. Blackman, J. W. Tukey.** Pathfinding work reprinted from "Bell System Technical Journal." Various ways of getting practically useful answers in power spectra measurement, using results from both transmission and statistical estimation theory. Treats: Autocovariance, Functions and Power Spectra, Distortion, Heterodyne Filtering, Smoothing, Decimation Procedures, Transversal Filtering, much more. Appendix reviews fundamental Fourier techniques. Index of notation. Glossary of terms. 24 figures. 12 tables. 192pp. 5⅜ x 8⅝.
S507 Paperbound **$1.85**

**TREATISE ON ELECTRICITY AND MAGNETISM, James Clerk Maxwell.** For more than 80 years a seemingly inexhaustible source of leads for physicists, mathematicians, engineers. Total of 1082pp. on such topics as Measurement of Quantities, Electrostatics, Elementary Mathematical Theory of Electricity, Electrical Work and Energy in a System of Conductors, General Theorems, Theory of Electrical Images, Electrolysis, Conduction, Polarization, Dielectrics, Resistance, much more. "The greatest mathematical physicist since Newton," Sir James Jeans. 3rd edition. 107 figures, 21 plates. 1082pp. 5⅜ x 8.
S186 Clothbound **$4.95**

# CHEMISTRY AND PHYSICAL CHEMISTRY

**THE PHASE RULE AND ITS APPLICATIONS, Alexander Findlay.** Covers chemical phenomena of 1 to 4 multiple component systems, the "standard work on the subject" (Nature). Completely revised, brought up to date by A. N. Campbell, N. O. Smith. New material on binary, tertiary liquid equilibria, solid solutions in ternary systems, quinary systems of salts, water, etc. Completely revised to triangular coordinates in ternary systems, clarified graphic representation, solid models, etc. 9th revised edition. 236 figures. 505 footnotes, mostly bibliographic. xii + 449pp. 5⅜ x 8.
S92 Paperbound **$2.45**

**DYNAMICAL THEORY OF GASES, James Jeans.** Divided into mathematical, physical chapters for convenience of those not expert in mathematics. Discusses mathematical theory of gas in steady state, thermodynamics, Bolzmann, Maxwell, kinetic theory, quantum theory, exponentials, etc. "One of the classics of scientific writing . . . as lucid and comprehensive an exposition of the kinetic theory as has ever been written," J. of Institute of Engineers. 4th enlarged edition, with new material on quantum theory, quantum dynamics, etc. 28 figures. 444pp. 6⅛ x 9¼.
S136 Paperbound **$2.45**

**POLAR MOLECULES, Pieter Debye.** Nobel laureate offers complete guide to fundamental electrostatic field relations, polarizability, molecular structure. Partial contents: electric intensity, displacement, force, polarization by orientation, molar polarization, molar refraction, halogen-hydrides, polar liquids, ionic saturation, dielectric constant, etc. Special chapter considers quantum theory. "Clear and concise . . . coordination of experimental results with theory will be readily appreciated," Electronics Industries. 172pp. 5⅜ x 8.
S63 Clothbound **$3.50**
S64 Paperbound **$1.50**

**ATOMIC SPECTRA AND ATOMIC STRUCTURE, G. Herzberg.** Excellent general survey for chemists, physicists specializing in other fields. Partial contents: simplest line spectra, elements of atomic theory; multiple structure of line spectra, electron spin; building-up principle, periodic system of elements; finer details of atomic spectra; hyperfine structure of spectral lines; some experimental results and applications. 80 figures. 20 tables. xiii + 257pp. 5⅜ x 8.
S115 Paperbound **$1.95**

**TREATISE ON THERMODYNAMICS, Max Planck.** Classic based on his original papers. Brilliant concepts of Nobel laureate make no assumptions regarding nature of heat, rejects special approaches of Helmholtz, Maxwell, to offer uniform point of view for entire field. Seminal work by founder of quantum theory, deducing new physical, chemical laws. A standard text, an excellent introduction to field for students with knowledge of elementary chemistry, physics, calculus. 3rd English edition. xvi + 297pp. 5⅜ x 8.
S219 Paperbound **$1.75**

**KINETIC THEORY OF LIQUIDS, J. Frenkel.** Regards kinetic theory of liquids as generalization, extension of theory of solid bodies, covers all types of arrangements of solids; thermal displacements of atoms; interstitial atoms, ions; orientational, rotational motion of molecules; transition between states of matter. Mathematical theory developed close to physical subject matter. "Discussed in a simple yet deeply penetrating fashion . . . will serve as seeds for a great many basic and applied developments in chemistry," J. of the Amer. Chemical Soc. 216 bibliographical footnotes. 55 figures. xi + 485pp. 5⅜ x 8.
S94 Clothbound **$3.95**
S95 Paperbound **$2.45**

# ASTRONOMY

**OUT OF THE SKY, H. H. Nininger.** Non-technical, comprehensive introduction to "meteoritics" —science concerned with arrival of matter from outer space. By one of world's experts on meteorites, this book defines meteors and meteorites; studies fireball clusters and processions, meteorite composition, size, distribution, showers, explosions, origins, much more. viii + 336pp. 5⅜ x 8.
T519 Paperbound **$1.85**

**AN INTRODUCTION TO THE STUDY OF STELLAR STRUCTURE, S. Chandrasekhar.** Outstanding treatise on stellar dynamics by one of greatest astro-physicists. Examines relationship between loss of energy, mass, and radius of stars in steady state. Discusses thermodynamic laws from Caratheodory's axiomatic standpoint; adiabatic, polytropic laws; work of Ritter, Emden, Kelvin, etc.; Stroemgren envelopes as starter for theory of gaseous stars; Gibbs statistical mechanics (quantum); degenerate stellar configuration, theory of white dwarfs; etc. "Highest level of scientific merit," Bulletin. Amer. Math. Soc. 33 figures. 509pp. 5⅜ x 8.
S413 Paperbound **$2.75**

**LES MÉTHODES NOVELLES DE LA MÉCANIQUE CÉLESTE, H. Poincaré.** Complete French text of one of Poincaré's most important works. Revolutionized celestial mechanics: first use of integral invariants, first major application of linear differential equations, study of periodic orbits, lunar motion and Jupiter's satellites, three body problem, and many other important topics. "Started a new era . . . so extremely modern that even today few have mastered his weapons," E. T. Bell. 3 volumes. Total 1282pp. 6⅛ x 9¼.
Vol. 1 S401 Paperbound **$2.75**
Vol. 2 S402 Paperbound **$2.75**
Vol. 3 S403 Paperbound **$2.75**
The set **$7.50**

**THE REALM OF THE NEBULAE, E. Hubble.** One of the great astronomers of our time presents his concept of "island universes," and describes its effect on astronomy. Covers velocity-distance relation; classification, nature, distances, general field of nebulae; cosmological theories; nebulae in the neighborhood of the Milky way; etc. 39 photos, including velocity-distance relations shown by spectrum comparison. "One of the most progressive lines of astronomical research," The Times, London. New Introduction by A. Sandage. 55 illustrations. xxiv + 201pp. 5⅜ x 8.
S455 Paperbound **$1.50**

**HOW TO MAKE A TELESCOPE, Jean Texereau.** Design, build an f/6 or f/8 Newtonian type reflecting telescope, with altazimuth Couder mounting, suitable for planetary, lunar, and stellar observation. Covers every operation step-by-step, every piece of equipment. Discusses basic principles of geometric and physical optics (unnecessary to construction), comparative merits of reflectors, refractors. A thorough discussion of eyepieces, finders, grinding, installation, testing, etc. 241 figures, 38 photos, show almost every operation and tool. Potential errors are anticipated. Foreword by A. Couder. Sources of supply. xiii + 191pp. 6¼ x 10.
T464 Clothbound **$3.50**

# BIOLOGICAL SCIENCES

**THE BIOLOGY OF THE AMPHIBIA, G. K. Noble,** Late Curator of Herpetology at Am. Mus. of Nat. Hist. Probably most used text on amphibia, most comprehensive, clear, detailed. 19 chapters, 85 page supplement: development; heredity; life history; speciation; adaptation; sex, integument, respiratory, circulatory, digestive, muscular, nervous systems; instinct, intelligence, habits, economic value classification, environment relationships, etc. "Nothing comparable to it," C. H. Pope, curator of Amphibia, Chicago Mus. of Nat. Hist. 1047 item bibliography. 174 illustrations. 600pp. 5⅜ x 8.
S206 Paperbound **$2.98**

**THE ORIGIN OF LIFE, A. I. Oparin.** A classic of biology. This is the first modern statement of theory of gradual evolution of life from nitrocarbon compounds. A brand-new evaluation of Oparin's theory in light of later research, by Dr. S. Margulis, University of Nebraska. xxv + 270pp. 5⅜ x 8.
S213 Paperbound **$1.75**

**THE BIOLOGY OF THE LABORATORY MOUSE, edited by G. D. Snell.** Prepared in 1941 by staff of Roscoe B. Jackson Memorial Laboratory, still the standard treatise on the mouse, assembling enormous amount of material for which otherwise you spend hours of research. Embryology, reproduction, histology, spontaneous neoplasms, gene and chromosomes mutations, genetics of spontaneous tumor formations, of tumor transplantation, endocrine secretion and tumor formation, milk influence and tumor formation, inbred, hybrid animals, parasites, infectious diseases, care and recording. "A wealth of information of vital concern. . . . recommended to all who could use a book on such a subject," Nature. Classified bibliography of 1122 items. 172 figures, including 128 photos. ix + 497pp. 6⅛ x 9¼.
S248 Clothbound **$6.00**

**THE TRAVELS OF WILLIAM BARTRAM, edited by Mark Van Doren.** Famous source-book of American anthropology, natural history, geography, is record kept by Bartram in 1770's on travels through wilderness of Florida, Georgia, Carolinas. Containing accurate, beautiful descriptions of Indians, settlers, fauna, flora, it is one of finest pieces of Americana ever written. 13 original illustrations. 448pp. 5⅜ x 8. T13 Paperbound **$2.00**

**BEHAVIOUR AND SOCIAL LIFE OF THE HONEYBEE, Ronald Ribbands.** Outstanding scientific study; a compendium of practically everything known of social life of honeybee. Stresses behaviour of individual bees in field, hive. Extends von Frisch's experiments on communication among bees. Covers perception of temperature, gravity, distance, vibration; sound production; glands; structural differences; wax production; temperature regulation; recognition, communication; drifting, mating behaviour, other highly interesting topics. "This valuable work is sure of a cordial reception by laymen, beekeepers and scientists," Prof. Karl von Frisch, Brit. J. of Animal Behaviour. Bibliography of 690 references. 127 diagrams, graphs, sections of bee anatomy, fine photographs. 352pp. S410 Clothbound **$4.50**

**ELEMENTS OF MATHEMATICAL BIOLOGY, A. J. Lotka.** Pioneer classic, 1st major attempt to apply modern mathematical techniques on large scale to phenomena of biology, biochemistry, psychology, ecology, similar life sciences. Partial contents: Statistical meaning of irreversibility; Evolution as redistribution; Equations of kinetics of evolving systems; Chemical, inter-species equilibrium; parameters of state; Energy transformers of nature, etc. Can be read with profit by even those having no advanced math; unsurpassed as study-reference. Formerly titled "Elements of Physical Biology." 72 figures. xxx + 460pp. 5⅜ x 8.
S346 Paperbound **$2.45**

**TREES OF THE EASTERN AND CENTRAL UNITED STATES AND CANADA, W. M. Harlow.** Serious middle-level text covering more than 140 native trees, important escapes, with information on general appearance, growth habit, leaf forms, flowers, fruit, bark, commercial use, distribution, habitat, woodlore, etc. Keys within text enable you to locate various species easily, to know which have edible fruit, much more useful, interesting information. "Well illustrated to make identification very easy," Standard Cat. for Public Libraries. Over 600 photographs, figures. xiii + 288pp. 5⅝ x 6½. T395 Paperbound **$1.35**

**FRUIT KEY AND TWIG KEY TO TREES AND SHRUBS (Fruit key to Northeastern Trees, Twig key to Deciduous Woody Plants of Eastern North America), W. M. Harlow.** Only guides with photographs of every twig, fruit described. Especially valuable to novice. Fruit key (both deciduous trees, evergreens) has introduction on seeding, organs involved, types, habits. Twig key introduction treats growth, morphology. In keys proper, identification is almost automatic. Exceptional work, widely used in university courses, especially useful for identification in winter, or from fruit or seed only. Over 350 photos, up to 3 times natural size. Index of common, scientific names, in each key. xvii + 125pp. 5⅝ x 8⅜. T511 Paperbound **$1.25**

**INSECT LIFE AND INSECT NATURAL HISTORY, S. W. Frost.** Unusual for emphasizing habits, social life, ecological relations of insects rather than more academic aspects of classification, morphology. Prof. Frost's enthusiasm and knowledge are everywhere evident as he discusses insect associations, specialized habits like leaf-rolling, leaf mining, case-making, the gall insects, boring insects, etc. Examines matters not usually covered in general works: insects as human food; insect music, musicians; insect response to radio waves; use of insects in art, literature. "Distinctly different, possesses an individuality all its own," Journal of Forestry. Over 700 illustrations. Extensive bibliography. x + 524pp. 5⅜ x 8.
T519 Paperbound **$2.49**

**A WAY OF LIFE, AND OTHER SELECTED WRITINGS, Sir William Osler.** Physician, humanist, Osler discusses brilliantly Thomas Browne, Gui Patin, Robert Burton, Michael Servetus, William Beaumont, Laennec. Includes such favorite writing as title essay, "The Old Humanities and the New Science," "Books and Men," "The Student Life," 6 more of his best discussions of philosophy, literature, religion. "The sweep of his mind and interests embraced every phase of human activity," G. L. Keynes. 5 photographs. Introduction by G. L. Keynes, M.D., F.R.C.S. xx + 278pp. 5⅜ x 8. T488 Paperbound **$1.50**

**THE GENETICAL THEORY OF NATURAL SELECTION, R. A. Fisher.** 2nd revised edition of vital reviewing of Darwin's Selection Theory in terms of particulate inheritance, by one of greatest authorities on experimental, theoretical genetics. Theory stated in mathematical form. Special features of particulate inheritance are examined: evolution of dominance, maintenance of specific variability, mimicry, sexual selection, etc. 5 chapters on man's special circumstances as a social animal. 16 photographs. x + 310pp. 5⅜ x 8.
S466 Paperbound **$1.85**

**THE AUTOBIOGRAPHY OF CHARLES DARWIN, AND SELECTED LETTERS, edited by Francis Darwin.** Darwin's own record of early life; historic voyage aboard "Beagle;" furore surrounding evolution, his replies; reminiscences of his son. Letters to Henslow, Lyell, Hooker, Huxley, Wallace, Kingsley, etc., and thoughts on religion, vivisection. We see how he revolutionized geology with concepts of ocean subsidence; how his great books on variation of plants and animals, primitive man, expression of emotion among primates, plant fertilization, carnivorous plants, protective coloration, etc., came into being. 365pp. 5⅜ x 8.
T479 Paperbound **$1.65**

**ANIMALS IN MOTION, Eadweard Muybridge.** Largest, most comprehensive selection of Muybridge's famous action photos of animals, from his "Animal Locomotion." 3919 high-speed shots of 34 different animals, birds, in 123 types of action; horses, mules, oxen, pigs, goats, camels, elephants, dogs, cats guanacos, sloths, lions, tigers, jaguars, raccoons, baboons, deer, elk, gnus, kangaroos, many others, walking, running, flying, leaping. Horse alone in over 40 ways. Photos taken against ruled backgrounds; most actions taken from 3 angles at once: 90°, 60°, rear. Most plates original size. Of considerable interest to scientists as biology classic, records of actual facts of natural history, physiology. "Really marvelous series of plates," Nature. "Monumental work," Waldemar Kaempffert. Edited by L. S. Brown, 74 page introduction on mechanics of motion. 340pp. of plates. 3919 photographs. 416pp. Deluxe binding, paper. (Weight: 4½ lbs.) 7⅛ x 10⅝.
T203 Clothbound **$10.00**

**THE HUMAN FIGURE IN MOTION, Eadweard Muybridge.** New edition of great classic in history of science and photography, largest selection ever made from original Muybridge photos of human action: 4789 photographs, illustrating 163 types of motion: walking, running, lifting, etc. in time-exposure sequence photos at speeds up to 1/6000th of a second. Men, women, children, mostly undraped, showing bone, muscle positions against ruled backgrounds, mostly taken at 3 angles at once. Not only was this a great work of photography, acclaimed by contemporary critics as work of genius, but it was also a great 19th century landmark in biological research. Historical introduction by Prof. Robert Taft, U. of Kansas. Plates original size, full of detail. Over 500 action strips. 407pp. 7¾ x 10⅝. Deluxe edition.
7204 Clothbound **$10.00**

**AN INTRODUCTION TO THE STUDY OF EXPERIMENTAL MEDICINE, Claude Bernard.** 90-year old classic of medical science, only major work of Bernard available in English, records his efforts to transform physiology into exact science. Principles of scientific research illustrated by specified case histories from his work; roles of chance, error, preliminary false conclusion, in leading eventually to scientific truth; use of hypothesis. Much of modern application of mathematics to biology rests on foundation set down here. "The presentation is polished . . . reading is easy," Revue des questions scientifiques. New foreword by Prof. I. B. Cohen, Harvard U. xxv + 266pp. 5⅜ x 8.
T400 Paperbound **$1.50**

**STUDIES ON THE STRUCTURE AND DEVELOPMENT OF VERTEBRATES, E. S. Goodrich.** Definitive study by greatest modern comparative anatomist. Exhaustive morphological, phylogenetic expositions of skeleton, fins, limbs, skeletal visceral arches, labial cartilages, visceral clefts, gills, vascular, respiratory, excretory, periphal nervous systems, etc., from fish to higher mammals. "For many a day this will certainly be the standard textbook on Vertebrate Morphology in the English language," Journal of Anatomy. 754 illustrations. 69 page biographical study by C. C. Hardy. Bibliography of 1186 references. Two volumes, total 906pp. 5⅜ x 8.
Two vol. set S449, 450 Paperbound **$5.00**

# EARTH SCIENCES

**THE EVOLUTION OF IGNEOUS BOOKS, N. L. Bowen.** Invaluable serious introduction applies techniques of physics, chemistry to explain igneous rock diversity in terms of chemical composition, fractional crystallization. Discusses liquid immiscibility in silicate magmas, crystal sorting, liquid lines of descent, fractional resorption of complex minerals, petrogen, etc. Of prime importance to geologists, mining engineers; physicists, chemists working with high temperature, pressures. "Most important," Times, London. 263 bibliographic notes. 82 figures. xviii + 334pp. 5⅜ x 8.
S311 Paperbound **$1.85**

**GEOGRAPHICAL ESSAYS, M. Davis.** Modern geography, geomorphology rest on fundamental work of this scientist. 26 famous essays present most important theories, field researches. Partial contents: Geographical Cycle; Plains of Marine, Subaerial Denudation; The Peneplain; Rivers, Valleys of Pennsylvania; Outline of Cape Cod; Sculpture of Mountains by Glaciers; etc. "Long the leader and guide," Economic Geography. "Part of the very texture of geography . . . models of clear thought," Geographic Review. 130 figures. vi + 777pp. 5⅜ x 8.
S383 Paperbound **$2.95**

**URANIUM PROSPECTING, H. L. Barnes.** For immediate practical use, professional geologist considers uranium ores, geological occurrences, field conditions, all aspects of highly profitable occupation. "Helpful information . . . easy-to-use, easy-to-find style," Geotimes. x + 117pp. 5⅜ x 8.
T309 Paperbound **$1.00**

**DE RE METALLICA, Georgius Agricola.** 400 year old classic translated, annotated by former President Herbert Hoover. 1st scientific study of mineralogy, mining, for over 200 years after its appearance in 1556 the standard treatise. 12 books, exhaustively annotated, discuss history of mining, selection of sites, types of deposits, making pits, shafts, ventilating, pumps, crushing machinery; assaying, smelting, refining metals; also salt alum, nitre, glass making. Definitive edition, with all 289 16th century woodcuts of original. Biographical, historical introductions. Bibliography, survey of ancient authors. Indexes. A fascinating book for anyone interested in art, history of science, geology, etc. Deluxe Edition. 289 illustrations. 672pp. 6¾ x 10. Library cloth.                                    S6 Clothbound **$10.00**

**INTERNAL CONSTITUTION OF THE EARTH, edited by Beno Gutenberg.** Prepared for National Research Council, this is a complete, thorough coverage of earth origins, continent formation, nature and behaviour of earth's core, petrology of crust, cooling forces in core, seismic and earthquake material, gravity, elastic constants, strain characteristics, similar topics. "One is filled with admiration . . . a high standard . . . there is no reader who will not learn something from this book," London, Edinburgh, Dublin, Philosophic Magazine. Largest Bibliography in print: 1127 classified items. Table of constants. 43 diagrams. 439pp. 6⅛ x 9¼.                                           S414 Paperbound **$2.45**

**THE BIRTH AND DEVELOPMENT OF THE GEOLOGICAL SCIENCES, F. D. Adams.** Most thorough history of earth sciences ever written. Geological thought from earliest times to end of 19th century, covering over 300 early thinkers and systems; fossils and their explanation, vulcanists vs. neptunists, figured stones and paleontology, generation of stones, dozens of similar topics. 91 illustrations, including Medieval, Renaissance woodcuts, etc. 632 footnotes, mostly bibliographical. 511pp. 5⅜ x 8.                               T5 Paperbound **$2.00**

**HYDROLOGY, edited by O. E. Meinzer,** prepared for the National Research Council. Detailed, complete reference library on precipitation, evaporation, snow, snow surveying, glaciers, lakes, infiltration, soil moisture, ground water, runoff, drought, physical changes produced by water hydrology of limestone terranes, etc. Practical in application, especially valuable for engineers. 24 experts have created "the most up-to-date, most complete treatment of the subject," Am. Assoc. of Petroleum Geologists. 165 illustrations. xi + 712pp. 6⅛ x 9¼.                                           S191 Paperbound **$2.95**

# LANGUAGE AND TRAVEL AIDS FOR SCIENTISTS

## SAY IT language phrase books

"SAY IT" in the foreign language of your choice! We have sold over ½ million copies of these popular, useful language books. They will not make you an expert linguist overnight, but they do cover most practical matters of everyday life abroad.

**Over 1000 useful phrases,** expressions, additional variants, substitutions.

**Modern! Useful!** Hundreds of phrases not available in other texts: "Nylon," "air-conditioned," etc.

The ONLY inexpensive phrase book **completely indexed.** Everything is available at a flip of your finger, ready to use.

Prepared by native linguists, travel experts.

Based on years of travel experience abroad.

May be used by itself, or to supplement any other text or course. Provides a living element. Used by many colleges, institutions: Hunter College; Barnard College; Army Ordinance School, Aberdeen; etc.

Available, 1 book per language:

**Danish** (T818) 75¢
**Dutch** (T817) 75¢
**English (for German-speaking people)** (T801) 60¢
**English (for Italian-speaking people)** (T816) 60¢
**English (for Spanish-speaking people)** (T802) 60¢
**Esperanto** (T820) 75¢
**French** (T803) 60¢
**German** (T804) 60¢
**Modern Greek** (T813) 75¢
**Hebrew** (T805) 60¢

**Italian** (T806) 60¢
**Japanese** (T807) 75¢
**Norwegian** (T814) 75¢
**Russian** (T810) 75¢
**Spanish** (T811) 60¢
**Turkish** (T821) 75¢
**Yiddish** (T815) 75¢
**Swedish** (T812) 75¢
**Polish** (T808) 75¢
**Portuguese** (T809) 75¢

**MONEY CONVERTER AND TIPPING GUIDE FOR EUROPEAN TRAVEL, C. Vomacka.** Purse-size handbook crammed with information on currency regulations, tipping for every European country, including Israel, Turkey, Czechoslovakia, Rumania, Egypt, Russia, Poland. Telephone, postal rates; duty-free imports, passports, visas, health certificates; foreign clothing sizes; weather tables. What, when to tip. 5th year of publication. 128pp. 3½ x 5¼.    T260 Paperbound **60¢**

**NEW RUSSIAN-ENGLISH AND ENGLISH-RUSSIAN DICTIONARY, M. A. O'Brien.** Unusually comprehensive guide to reading, speaking, writing Russian, for both advanced, beginning students. Over 70,000 entries in new orthography, full information on accentuation, grammatical classifications. Shades of meaning, idiomatic uses, colloquialisms, tables of irregular verbs for both languages. Individual entries indicate stems, transitiveness, perfective, imperfective aspects, conjugation, sound changes, accent, etc. Includes pronunciation instruction. Used at Harvard, Yale, Cornell, etc. 738pp. 5⅜ x 8.    T208 Paperbound **$2.00**

**PHRASE AND SENTENCE DICTIONARY OF SPOKEN RUSSIAN, English-Russian, Russian-English.** Based on phrases, complete sentences, not isolated words—recognized as one of best methods of learning idiomatic speech. Over 11,500 entries, indexed by single words, over 32,000 English, Russian sentences, phrases, in immediately useable form. Shows accent changes in conjugation, declension; irregular forms listed both alphabetically, under main form of word. 15,000 word introduction covers Russian sounds, writing, grammar, syntax. 15 page appendix of geographical names, money, important signs, given names, foods, special Soviet terms, etc. Originally published as U.S. Gov't Manual TM 30-944. iv + 573pp. 5⅜ x 8.    T496 Paperbound **$2.75**

**PHRASE AND SENTENCE DICTIONARY OF SPOKEN SPANISH, Spanish-English, English-Spanish.** Compiled from spoken Spanish, based on phrases, complete sentences rather than isolated words—not an ordinary dictionary. Over 16,000 entries indexed under single words, both Castilian, Latin-American. Language in immediately useable form. 25 page introduction provides rapid survey of sounds, grammar, syntax, full consideration of irregular verbs. Especially apt in modern treatment of phrases, structure. 17 page glossary gives translations of geographical names, money values, numbers, national holidays, important street signs, useful expressions of high frequency, plus unique 7 page glossary of Spanish, Spanish-American foods. Originally published as U.S. Gov't Manual TM 30-900. iv + 513pp. 5⅜ x 8⅜.    T495 Paperbound **$1.75**

## SAY IT CORRECTLY language record sets

The best inexpensive pronunciation aids on the market. Spoken by native linguists associated with major American universities, each record contains:

14 minutes of speech—12 minutes of normal, relatively slow speech, 2 minutes of normal conversational speed.

120 basic phrases, sentences, covering nearly every aspect of everyday life, travel—introducing yourself, travel in autos, buses, taxis, etc., walking, sightseeing, hotels, restaurants, money, shopping, etc.

32 page booklet containing everything on record plus English translations easy-to-follow phonetic guide.

Clear, high-fidelity recordings.

Unique bracketing systems, selection of basic sentences enabling you to expand use of SAY IT CORRECTLY records with a dictionary, to fit thousands of additional situations.

Use this record to supplement any course or text. All sounds in each language illustrated perfectly—imitate speaker in pause which follows each foreign phrase in slow section, and be amazed at increased ease, accuracy of pronounciation. Available, one language per record for

| | | |
|---|---|---|
| **French** | **Spanish** | **German** |
| **Italian** | **Dutch** | **Modern Greek** |
| **Japanese** | **Russian** | **Portuguese** |
| **Polish** | **Swedish** | **Hebrew** |
| **English (for German-speaking people)** | | **English (for Spanish-speaking people)** |

7″ (33 1/3 rpm) record, album, booklet. **$1.00 each.**

**SPEAK MY LANGUAGE: SPANISH FOR YOUNG BEGINNERS, M. Ahlman, Z. Gilbert.** Records provide one of the best, most entertaining methods of introducing a foreign language to children. Within framework of train trip from Portugal to Spain, an English-speaking child is introduced to Spanish by native companion. (Adapted from successful radio program of N.Y. State Educational Department.) A dozen different categories of expressions,. including greeting, numbers, time, weather, food, clothes, family members, etc. Drill is combined with poetry and contextual use. Authentic background music. Accompanying book enables a reader to follow records, includes vocabulary of over 350 recorded expressions. Two 10″ 33 1/3 records, total of 40 minutes. Book. 40 illustrations. 69pp. 5¼ x 10½.    T890 The set **$4.95**

## LISTEN & LEARN language record sets

LISTEN & LEARN is the only extensive language record course designed especially to meet your travel and everyday needs. Separate sets for each language, each containing three 33 1/3 rpm long-playing records—1 1/2 hours of recorded speech by eminent native speakers who are professors at Columbia, New York U., Queens College.

Check the following features found only in LISTEN & LEARN:

> Dual language recording. 812 selected phrases, sentences, over 3200 words, spoken first in English, then foreign equivalent. Pause after each foreign phrase allows time to repeat expression.

> 128-page manual (196 page for Russian)—everything on records, plus simple transcription. Indexed for convenience. Only set on the market completely indexed.

> Practical. No time wasted on material you can find in any grammar. No dead words. Covers central core material with phrase approach. Ideal for person with limited time. Living, modern expressions, not found in other courses. Hygienic products, modern equipment, shopping, "air-conditioned," etc. Everything is immediately useable.

> High-fidelity recording, equal in clarity to any costing up to $6 per record.

"Excellent . . . impress me as being among the very best on the market," Prof. Mario Pei, Dept. of Romance Languages, Columbia U. "Inexpensive and well done . . . ideal present," Chicago Sunday Tribune. "More genuinely helpful than anything of its kind," Sidney Clark, well-known author of "All the Best" travel books.

**UNCONDITIONAL GUARANTEE.** Try LISTEN & LEARN, then return it within 10 days for full refund, if you are not satisfied. It is guaranteed after you actually use it.

6 modern languages—FRENCH, SPANISH, GERMAN, ITALIAN, RUSSIAN, or JAPANESE *—one language to each set of 3 records (33 1/3 rpm). 128 page manual. Album.

| | | | | | |
|---|---|---|---|---|---|
| **Spanish** | the set $4.95 | **German** | the set $4.95 | **Japanese*** | the set $5.95 |
| **French** | the set $4.95 | **Italian** | the set $4.95 | **Russian** | the set $5.95 |

* Available Oct. 1959.

## TRÜBNER COLLOQUIAL SERIES

These unusual books are members of the famous Trübner series of colloquial manuals. They have been written to provide adults with a sound colloquial knowledge of a foreign language, and are suited for either class use or self-study. Each book is a complete course in itself, with progressive, easy to follow lessons. Phonetics, grammar, and syntax are covered, while hundreds of phrases and idioms, reading texts, exercises, and vocabulary are included. These books are unusual in being neither skimpy nor overdetailed in grammatical matters, and in presenting up-to-date, colloquial, and practical phrase material. Bilingual presentation is stressed, to make thorough self-study easier for the reader.

**COLLOQUIAL HINDUSTANI, A. H. Harley,** formerly Nizam's Reader in Urdu, U. of London. 30 pages on phonetics and scripts (devanagari & Arabic-Persian) are followed by 29 lessons, including material on English and Arabic-Persian influences. Key to all exercises. Vocabulary. 5 x 7½. 147pp. Clothbound **$1.75**

**COLLOQUIAL ARABIC, DeLacy O'Leary.** Foremost Islamic scholar covers language of Egypt, Syria, Palestine, & Northern Arabia. Extremely clear coverage of complex Arabic verbs & noun plurals; also cultural aspects of language. Vocabulary. xviii + 192pp. 5 x 7½. Clothbound **$1.75**

**COLLOQUIAL GERMAN, P. F. Doring.** Intensive thorough coverage of grammar in easily-followed form. Excellent for brush-up, with hundreds of colloquial phrases. 34 pages of bilingual texts. 224pp. 5 x 7½. Clothbound **$1.75**

**COLLOQUIAL SPANISH, W. R. Patterson.** Castilian grammar and colloquial language, loaded with bilingual phrases and colloquialisms. Excellent for review or self-study. 164pp. 5 x 7½. Clothbound **$1.75**

**COLLOQUIAL FRENCH, W. R. Patterson.** 16th revised edition of this extremely popular manual. Grammar explained with model clarity, and hundreds of useful expressions and phrases; exercises, reading texts, etc. Appendixes of new and useful words and phrases. 223pp. 5 x 7½. Clothbound **$1.75**

# DOVER SCIENCE BOOKS

**COLLOQUIAL PERSIAN, L. P. Elwell-Sutton.** Best introduction to modern Persian, with 90 page grammatical section followed by conversations, 35 page vocabulary. 139pp.    Clothbound **$1.75**

**COLLOQUIAL CZECH, J. Schwarz,** former headmaster of Lingua Institute, Prague. Full easily followed coverage of grammar, hundreds of immediately useable phrases, texts. Perhaps the best Czech grammar in print. "An absolutely successful textbook," JOURNAL OF CZECHO-SLOVAK FORCES IN GREAT BRITAIN. 252pp. 5 x 7½.    Clothbound **$2.50**

**COLLOQUIAL RUMANIAN, G. Nandris,** Professor of University of London. Extremely thorough coverage of phonetics, grammar, syntax; also included 70 page reader, and 70 page vocabulary. Probably the best grammar for this increasingly important language. 340pp. 5 x 7½.
    Clothbound **$2.50**

**COLLOQUIAL ITALIAN, A. L. Hayward.** Excellent self-study course in grammar, vocabulary, idioms, and reading. Easy progressive lessons will give a good working knowledge of Italian in the shortest possible time. 5 x 7½.    Clothbound **$1.75**

# MISCELLANEOUS

**TREASURY OF THE WORLD'S COINS, Fred Reinfeld.** Finest general introduction to numismatics; non-technical, thorough, always fascinating. Coins of Greece, Rome, modern countries of every continent, primitive societies, such oddities as 200-lb stone money of Yap, nail coinage of New England; all mirror man's economy, customs, religion, politics, philosophy, art. Entertaining, absorbing study; novel view of history. Over 750 illustrations. Table of value of coins illustrated. List of U.S. coin clubs. 224pp. 6½ x 9¼.
    T433 Paperbound **$1.75**

**ILLUSIONS AND DELUSIONS OF THE SUPERNATURAL AND THE OCCULT, D. H. Rawcliffe.** Rationally examines hundreds of persistent delusions including witchcraft, trances, mental healing, peyotl, poltergeists, stigmata, lycanthropy, live burial, auras, Indian rope trick, spiritualism, dowsing, telepathy, ghosts, ESP, etc. Explains, exposes mental, physical deceptions involved, making this not only an exposé of supernatural phenomena, but a valuable exposition of characteristic types of abnormal psychology. Originally "The Psychology of the Occult." Introduction by Julian Huxley. 14 illustrations. 551pp. 5⅜ x 8.
    T503 Paperbound **$2.00**

**HOAXES, C. D. MacDougall.** Shows how art, science, history, journalism can be perverted for private purposes. Hours of delightful entertainment, a work of scholarly value, often shocking. Examines hundreds of nonsense news, Cardiff giant, Shakespeare forgeries, Loch Ness monster, biblical frauds, political schemes, literary hoaxers like Chatterton, Ossian, disumbrationist school of painting, lady in black at Valentino's tomb, over 250 others. Will probably reveal truth about few things you've believed, will help you spot more easily the editorial "gander" or planted publicity release. "A stupendous collection . . . and shrewd analysis," New Yorker. New revised edition. 54 photographs. 320pp. 5⅜ x 8.    T465 Paperbound **$1.75**

**YOGA: A SCIENTIFIC EVALUATION, Kovoor T. Behanan.** Book that for first time gave Western readers a sane, scientific explanation, analysis of yoga. Author draws on laboratory experiments, personal records of year as disciple of yoga, to investigate yoga psychology, physiology, "supernatural" phenomena, ability to plumb deepest human powers. In this study under auspices of Yale University Institute of Human Relations, strictest principles of physiological, psychological inquiry are followed. Foreword by W. A. Miles, Yale University. 17 photographs. xx + 270pp. 5⅜ x 8.    T505 Paperbound **$1.65**

## Write for free catalogs!

*Indicate your field of interest. Dover publishes books on physics, earth sciences, mathematics, engineering, chemistry, astronomy, anthropology, biology, psychology, philosophy, religion, history, literature, mathematical recreations, languages, crafts, art, graphic arts, etc.*

*Write to Dept. catr*
*Dover Publications, Inc.*
*180 Varick St., N. Y. 14, N. Y.*

Science B

**Date Due**